CRASH

STORIES FROM THE EMERGENCY ROOM

VOLUME 3

DAVID BERG, M.D.

FREE REIGN
Publishing

CONTENTS

INTRODUCTION

The emergency room is a place of chaos, trauma, and sometimes, miracles. It's where people from all walks of life arrive in their most vulnerable moments, seeking help for everything from minor injuries to life-threatening emergencies. In the ER, minutes can mean the difference between life and death, and split-second decisions carry heavy consequences.

In *Crash: Stories from the Emergency Room*, nurses, doctors, and other ER staff share their most intense, devastating, uplifting, and bizarre experiences from their time in the trenches. From gruesome traumas to emotional reunions to feats of medical heroism, these stories shine a light on those who work tirelessly to save lives when minutes matter most.

Through these dramatic accounts, readers will gain

insight into what really happens behind the scenes in a busy emergency department. The chaos, urgency, frustrations, and triumphs of emergency medicine come to life in these pages. Alongside moments of devastating heartbreak are stories of hope, perseverance, and the power of human connection during crisis.

Crash offers a rare, unfiltered look inside the organized chaos of the ER. These stories celebrate the unsung heroes who confront the worst of humanity with empathy and compassion. Their experiences on the front lines reveal both the fragility and tenacity of human life. For anyone curious about what it's like to work in emergency medicine, or who enjoys an up-close look at suspenseful, moving stories of life-and-death drama, *Crash* delivers an adrenaline-packed read.

If you have a story from your time in the medical field, please message me at authorenterprisesllc@gmail.com. It just might end up in a future book of mine.

All the best.

Dr. David Berg

CHAPTER ONE

STUCK ON YOU

IN THE HEART OF WACO, Texas, I was no stranger to the chaos of medical emergencies. As a doctor working at one of the local hospitals, I had grown accustomed to the steady stream of patients who came through our doors seeking treatment for everything from farm accidents to construction mishaps.

However, In 2013, we had witnessed the worst of construction accidents. It was April 17th when an ammonium nitrate explosion shook the nearby town of West, Texas, roughly 18 miles north of Waco. The tragedy unfolded while emergency services personnel were responding to a fire at the West Fertilizer Company storage and distribution facility. Fifteen people lost their lives that day, more than 160 were injured, and over 150 buildings were damaged or destroyed. Our scanners had gone crazy that day, and we had seen the unimaginable.

That day had forever changed the way we prepared for emergencies, especially those involving construction sites. We knew that every second counted, and our team had become experts in rapid response and trauma care. We never wanted to be caught off guard again.

However, today, the scanners crackled with reports, and my heart skipped a beat when I heard that all-too-familiar alert: "Construction accident." I immediately sprang into action, rallying my medical team to meet the incoming ambulance at the hospital doors. Time was of the essence, and we had to be prepared for anything.

The wailing sirens of the ambulance, like a frenetic orchestra of urgency, pierced the air as it careened to a halt just outside the hospital's emergency entrance. With practiced precision, our team of medical professionals, rushed forward to fling open the heavy doors of the ambulance.

As the hospital's automatic sliding doors whispered open, the peculiar sight before us seized our collective attention—a patient, quite literally encased in cement, had just been wheeled in. The tale that unfolded was as bewildering as it was audacious. It all began at a construction site, where bravado and dares danced like sparks amidst the cacophony of heavy machinery.

The patient had accepted a challenge that defied the realm of rationality. The dare, as it were, involved plunging into a colossal vat of wet cement, an invitation to submerge oneself in the raw, formless substance that held the potential to transform into the foundations of buildings. Against all odds, and to the incredulity of onlookers, he had embraced this audacious challenge. His audacious leap had consequences as swift as they were bizarre, leading to his unexpected entrapment within the unforgiving clutches of the curing concrete.

As we gathered around the patient, now resembling a modern-day statue frozen in time, the hospital's energy momentarily ceased, replaced by a hushed anticipation. His body was enshrouded in the gray, heavy cocoon of cement, leaving only his face exposed—a visage etched with a combination of determination and disbelief. Amidst the surrealness of the situation, our dedicated team of medical professionals sprang into action.

Firefighters at the scene had chipped away at the hardened cement, but a substantial amount still clung to his body. The doctors on my team carefully evaluated his condition, trying to figure out where to begin the daunting task of saving him.

The residents were working on the patient, slowly chipping away at the concrete, and asking for the patient to explain what he was doing. He tells us that he's normally the smart one, not the guy who'd jump into a tub of cement because of a girl. I couldn't help but overhear the conversation and I asked if it was the same girl who came in with them and he said yes that the guys dared him and she was watching.

After much deliberation, we finally began our work. Dr. Marcus, our dermatologist, applied vinegar to the patient's skin to minimize the burning caused by the cement. It was a small relief for the young man who must have been in excruciating pain. While I worked, Dr. Klien, our general surgeon, offered words of encouragement, assuring the patient that more than just this one piece of his life defined him.

Dr. Klein had a feeling that something was off. She thought about it, running various scenarios through her head. She knew the answer was obvious, but just couldn't put her finger on it. As we painstakingly removed the larger chunks of cement, Dr. Klien suddenly realized that something crucial was missing. She couldn't put her finger on it at first, but then it hit her. His bladder was under immense pressure, and we needed to insert a catheter urgently to prevent it from rupturing. Finally, Dr. Klein realized it's the hydration - they've been feeding him fluids for four hours and left him with no way to urinate. The patient's bladder could explode. We had hydrated the patient to prevent dehydration, but we hadn't given him a way to release urine.

Dr. Klien, a distinguished hepatologist known for her expertise in liver diseases, furrowed her brows as she examined the patient's medical charts. She couldn't help but worry about the patient's liver, an organ that had been battered and bruised by a cascade of unforeseen events. As the guardian of the patient's liver function, she understood that the clock was ticking, and every moment counted.

Beside her stood Dr. Marcus, an experienced burn specialist whose eyes were locked onto the patient's scorched skin. The burns were extensive, a painful reminder of the perilous jump into a vat of molten material. Dr. Marcus knew that the road to recovery would be arduous, but his unwavering commitment to healing burned even brighter than the flames that had seared the patient's flesh. He felt the urgency of his expertise, knowing that the patient's life hung in the balance.

Dr. Eric, a seasoned intensivist who thrived in the chaos of the emergency room, was the voice of reason in this high-stakes scenario. He understood that beyond the specific concerns of liver and burns, the patient's overall condition was perilous. With a demeanor forged by countless life-or-death situations, he calmly explained that the patient's compromised circulation was a ticking time bomb. The toxins that had built up within his body threatened to silence his heart, and the only path forward was a united effort from all three doctors.

The rescue workers chipped away at the cement as the doctors tried to stabilize him. I had to do a fasciotomy on his leg to relieve the pressure and restore blood flow. Once Dr. Klein shed the light on his bladder issues, they had to put in a catheter to relieve the pressure so his bladder wouldn't explode.

I was faced with a challenging task. I had to perform a fasciotomy to relieve the pressure building up in the patient's leg. The cement had caused severe swelling, and the risk of muscle and tissue damage was significant.

The hospital's corridors seemed to pulse with urgency, every second ticking away like a metronome signaling a race against time. The patient, still encased in the unforgiving grip of the cement that had dared him, lay on the operating table. The room was charged with palpable tension as the medical team, led by the trio of Dr. Klien, Dr. Marcus, and Dr. Eric, meticulously continued their work.

With great care, they had already removed most of the cement, fragment by stubborn fragment, all while monitoring the patient's vital signs like hawks. It was a delicate dance, a high stakes juggling act where one wrong move could tip the precarious balance. As the final, obstinate chunk of cement was gingerly extracted, the patient's condition plummeted, just as predicted. His body was grappling with the sudden release of toxins that had built up during his cement entombment.

There was no room for hesitation. With a well-coordinated precision born of countless hours of training and experience, the medical team sprang into action. The rhythmic beeping of machines filled the room as they swiftly intubated the patient, securing his airway and ensuring that oxygen continued to flow into his lungs. Amidst this whirlwind of activity, the patient was wheeled out of the room and rushed down the sterile corridors, destined for the operating room where a team of skilled surgeons stood ready to address the myriad injuries that had resulted from his audacious escapade. It was a race against time, a symphony of skill and determination, and every heartbeat seemed to echo with the hope of saving a life hanging in the balance.

In surgery, the patient faced yet another life-threatening complication—a pulmonary embolism. Dr. Miller, our cardiovascular surgeon, instinctively reached for his pager to call in Dr. Kahn. But a resident stepped forward confidently, stating that she could handle the situation. Dr. Miller allowed her to proceed. We watched with bated breath as she skillfully resolved the embolus.

After a grueling surgery to address the myriad

injuries caused by his audacious plunge into cement, the patient emerged from the operating room. We had navigated the treacherous waters of uncertainty, and he had survived the initial ordeal. Yet, his journey to recovery was far from over. With utmost care, we transferred him to the Intensive Care Unit, where a vigilant team of healthcare professionals would continue to monitor his progress.

CHAPTER TWO

SILENT NIGHT

IT WAS a cold and snowy night in Nashville, and I found myself in the emergency room once again on Christmas Eve. I always took the Christmas Eve shift at the hospital. It was a silent night, a quiet night. Since I had no family to celebrate with, I volunteered so others could enjoy the holidays with their loved ones. The hallways were adorned with paper snowflakes and colorful garlands, and I was expecting a peaceful night of tending to minor injuries and seasonal ailments.

Little did I know, this Christmas Eve was about to take an unexpected turn. The ER had been unusually quiet with very little traffic, and I was just beginning to settle into the idea of a tranquil shift when the sound of screeching tires and shattering glass shattered the peaceful atmosphere.

A damaged limousine careened into the ambulance bay, its front end mangled, and glass shattered. I rushed outside, adrenaline pumping, and my breath visible in the freezing air. The driver's side door opened, and a disheveled woman in a blood-soaked evening gown stumbled out, her face etched with panic.

"I drove all by myself," she stammered, her voice trembling. Her eyes were wide with shock and fear. "We're not the patients. It's Danny, our driver. He's hurt, badly."

I turned my attention to the car and saw another woman in the back seat. She had a man's head wrapped in the ballgown dress she was wearing and was covered with blood. The driver was lying in her lap, his head wounds still soaking through her ivory gown.

I called out for a gurney and medical supplies as I rushed over to assess the situation. The women explained that the car in front of them had hit a patch of ice, sending it into a spin and skid. When the driver tried to brake, the limo lost control, and it too began to spin wildly on the icy road. Desperate to avoid a more catastrophic accident, the driver steered the limo off the road and down a steep embankment.

The limousine came to a crashing halt when it collided with a parked car on the street below. The impact had thrown the driver through the front wind-

shield, leaving him with his head wedged in the shattered glass.

The two passengers, clearly shaken but determined,
had managed to extract the driver from the windshield,
but his condition was dire. They pulled him back into
the limo. They had called 911 from their mobile phone
but were growing increasingly desperate as no one had
shown up.

In the back of the limousine, the elegantly dressed
woman was holding onto the driver, her eyes filled with
concern. She implored me to help him, and without hesitation, I directed Dr. Jones to apply pressure to the
driver's head wound while two interns assisted the other
women out of the vehicle.

As I assessed the patient's condition, it became clear
that he had sustained severe injuries. He had multiple
crush injuries, and the source of his bleeding was his
abdomen. My heart sank as I realized that he also had a
hemopericardium, a life-threatening condition where
blood accumulates around the heart.

In addition to hemopericardium, the driver was
faced with other life threatening injuries. One of the
most immediate and critical areas of concern when a
patient partially goes through a windshield is head
trauma. The impact with the glass surface can impart
substantial forces to the head, leading to a range of

injuries, including skull fractures, brain contusions, and traumatic brain injuries. The severity of these injuries can vary greatly, but given the potential for life-threatening complications, such as hemorrhage or increased intracranial pressure, urgent medical intervention is often required. As I examined the patient, it was crucial to assess his neurological status and order diagnostic imaging, such as a CT scan, to thoroughly evaluate the extent of the head trauma.

The driver was also facing several facial injuries. The driver's face was vulnerable to injury due to the direct impact, resulting in lacerations, fractures of the facial bones, including the nose, jaw, and cheekbones, and soft tissue damage. Comprehensive assessment of facial injuries is essential to determine the need for surgical repair and to address potential complications, particularly in the context of the patient's traumatic entry through the windshield. I wasn't able to visually assess the state of his injuries due to massive facial swelling and blood loss.

The emergency room became a whirlwind of activity as we swiftly but carefully prepared him for surgery.

The patient's internal injuries were extensive, a testament to the sheer force of the collision. The high-velocity impact had caused severe crush injuries to his chest and abdomen, leading to fractured ribs and potentially life-threatening bleeding. In addition, the windshield's glass shards had inflicted deep lacerations across his torso.

The entrance of the operating room was a portal to a world of controlled chaos. As the patient was carefully wheeled through the double doors, the bright surgical lights flickered to life, casting a sterile, fluorescent glow over the room. The air was cool and crisp, filled with the antiseptic scent that permeated every corner of the hospital. The stainless-steel instruments gleamed under the lights, meticulously arranged on sterile trays, ready to be wielded by skilled hands. The monitors blinked with vital signs, their rhythmic beeps serving as a constant reminder of the urgency of our mission.

Inside the operating room, I donned my surgical gown and gloves, the swish of fabric and snap of latex breaking the silence. My focus was unwavering as I meticulously scrubbed my hands, each stroke a ritual of cleanliness and precision. The sound of running water and the medicinal scent of surgical soap filled the room as I scrubbed away any potential contaminants. The surgical team bustled around, each member playing a vital role in the delicate ballet that was about to unfold. An anesthesiologist prepared to administer anesthesia while nurses readied the sterile drapes and instruments.

The patient's life was hanging by a thread. I was leading the team of surgeons. Together with the nurses, we worked meticulously to address each injury. As the minutes turned into hours, the surgical team's expertise and collective effort became our greatest hope in the face of this medical emergency.

Time became an unrelenting adversary as we fought to stabilize the patient, the victim of the icy Christmas Eve Car Wreck. The dimly lit emergency room seemed to echo with the urgency of our mission, with every tick of the clock a reminder that the patient's life hung precariously in the balance.

As I led the charge in the operating room, I felt the weight of responsibility that rested upon my shoulders. The patient's internal injuries were extensive and severe. The high-velocity impact had wreaked havoc within his chest and abdomen, resulting in shattered ribs and the ominous specter of life-threatening hemorrhage. The jagged remnants of the windshield had inflicted deep, jagged lacerations across his torso, adding another layer of complexity to the intricate web of injuries that threatened to overwhelm him.

The operating room itself seemed to pulse with tension as our surgical team worked diligently. Minutes turned into hours, the atmosphere in the operating room was fraught with intensity, yet there was an unwavering focus on the task at hand. The patient's life depended on our collective expertise and our ability to navigate this complex and perilous medical emergency. The steady hum of medical equipment, the measured voices of the surgical team, and the knowledge that we were fighting to restore life on this silent Christmas Eve night were the elements that defined that unforgettable medical adventure.

Inside the operating room, a tension hung heavy in the air as we embarked on our battle to save the patient's life. The surgical team worked with a synchronized precision that only years of training and countless hours of practice could achieve. They handed me sterile instruments, their gloved hands moving with grace and efficiency. The atmosphere was one of unwavering focus, where every action was deliberate, and every decision carried the weight of life and death.

In the background, the anesthesiologist was performing their critical task with a steady hand. The gentle hiss of anesthetic gases filled the room as they expertly administered the medication that would induce a deep slumber, ensuring that the patient felt no pain during the procedure. The anesthesia machine stood as a sentinel, its monitors and gauges diligently tracking the patient's vital signs, providing a constant stream of information to guide the anesthesiologist's actions. It was a delicate dance between consciousness and oblivion, and in this moment, the anesthesiologist's expertise turned into the only Christmas dance the patient was attending that night.

The monitors that surrounded us became the orchestra of the patient's fate. They blinked rhythmically with vital signs, their beeping forming a steady cadence. Heart rate, blood pressure, oxygen saturation—all were displayed in vivid, real-time data. Each blip on the screens was a pulse of hope.

Yet, despite the symphony of medical technology, the harsh reality remained unchanged. The patient's injuries were too extensive, and the trauma he had suffered was an insurmountable obstacle. As we stood in the silence of the night, we tried in vain to save his life. The injuries were too severe, and the driver turned and went down the road less traveled.

CHAPTER THREE

THE BIC

AFTER YEARS of dedicated service as an Army Doctor, leaving Fort Hood and venturing into private practice in Waco, Texas was both a momentous transition and a heartfelt decision. My military career had been defined by a sense of duty, discipline, and unwavering commitment to providing medical care to our brave soldiers and their families. The experiences and skills I had gained while serving in the Army had forged me into a seasoned physician, well-prepared to face the challenges that awaited in the civilian medical world.

My days at Fort Hood had been marked by the unique demands of military medicine, where I had treated a wide array of injuries and illnesses, often in high-pressure and austere environments. From providing medical support during field exercises to caring for soldiers on deployment in far-flung corners of the world, I honed my abilities as a doctor and learned to adapt to the unexpected. The transition to private practice brought its own set of challenges. While the environments and patient populations may have changed, my commitment to delivering the highest standard of care remained unwavering. It was with this dedication that I entered the bustling ER in Waco, ready to face the uncertainties of civilian medical practice.

My role as an ER doctor in Waco, Texas, had accustomed me to the unpredictable nature of emergency medicine. On this particular day, the usual flow of cases took an abrupt turn when a trauma alert for Donald, a middle-aged man, flashed across our screens. The urgency of the notification instantly shifted the atmosphere in the emergency room.

The patient's predicament was grave. He had been involved in a catastrophic car accident, the extent of which was apparent when he was wheeled into the hospital. A pen had been inserted into his throat to facilitate breathing, a stark indicator of the severity of his injuries. The collision had crushed his trachea, making it impossible for him to breathe on his own. Adding to the complexity of his situation, he also presented with a bruised kidney and a lacerated liver, further compounding the challenges we faced in our efforts to save his life.

As the trauma team swung into action, their efforts were nothing short of synchronized chaos. The urgency in the room was palpable as we worked together to stabilize the patient. Every second that ticked away seemed to hang heavily in the air, and we were acutely aware that his life teetered on the precipice of uncertainty. The injuries we had to contend with were multifaceted; aside from the crushed trachea, the patient's bruised kidney and lacerated liver added layers of complexity to his precarious condition.

Amid the whirlwind of activity, Dr. Bates, our proficient ear, nose, and throat specialist, emerged as a crucial figure in the patient's journey toward recovery. It was under his expertise that we faced the heart-wrenching reality that the patient's vocal cords had sustained irreparable damage. The news of this irreversible loss hung heavily in the room, casting a shadow over the emergency room's intense atmosphere. the patient, who had already endured the trauma of the car accident, now had to grapple with the reality of a life forever silenced. It was a profound and heartbreaking dimension to his ordeal, one that emphasized the fragility of human existence even in the face of modern medicine's best efforts.

The decision to proceed with surgery weighed

heavily on my shoulders, but it was clear that time was of the essence. With the clock ticking, I resolved to operate on the patient and began the process of meticulously preparing for the impending procedure. As I stood at the sink, the sensation of the lukewarm water cascading over my hands and forearms was a familiar prelude to the high-stakes surgery ahead. My mind raced through the intricate steps I would need to undertake to navigate the complex web of injuries that the patient had suffered.

Entering the operating room, the atmosphere was one of intense focus and determination. The sterile environment buzzed with the anticipation of the surgery ahead. The gleaming surgical instruments, laid out with precision, served as a stark reminder of the gravity of the situation. As I began the delicate procedure to repair the patient's crushed trachea, I couldn't help but reflect on the enormity of the task at hand. The pen, though a temporary solution to help him breathe, was no substitute for the restoration of his natural airway.

Stepping into the operating room, the gravity of the situation weighed on me, as well as the entire surgical team. The sterile environment was illuminated with the cold, white light of medical precision, and the meticulously arranged surgical instruments stood ready, gleaming like silent sentinels. Behind our masks and gowns, my colleagues and I knew that this was a defining moment in the patient's fight for survival.

As I embarked on the delicate procedure to repair the patient's crushed trachea, my hands moved with the precision and focus that came from years of training and experience. Each incision and suture brought us one step closer to the restoration of his natural airway. The pen, while a temporary solution to maintain his breathing, was a reminder of the urgency of our mission.

In the midst of the surgery to restore the patient's damaged trachea, an unexpected nightmare unfurled before our eyes—a surgeon's worst-case scenario. The sterile environment, which had been a bastion of control and precision, suddenly transformed into a battlefield as the patient's vital signs plunged alarmingly. Panic threatened to take hold, but the collective training and experience of the surgical team kicked in with unwavering resolve.

At that critical moment, I urgently summoned everyone in the room to conduct a meticulous search of the patient's body, a desperate bid to identify the elusive source of the internal bleeding that was rapidly sapping his life force. It was a race against time, and the atmosphere in the room crackled with tension. Dr. Smithe, one of our skilled general surgeons, emerged as a crucial figure in the unfolding drama. With deft hands and intuitive touch, he zeroed in on an area above the liver that felt ominously hard and distended, a clear indication that it was the epicenter of the life-threatening hemorrhage. The discovery sent shockwaves through the room, as we realized the dire implications of this hidden complication that had exacerbated the patient's already deteriorating condition.

With a surgeon's instinct and precision, he pinpointed an area just above the liver that felt unnaturally hard and distended. It was the proverbial needle in the haystack, and as our hearts pounded in our chests, the realization hit us like a thunderbolt. This was the epicenter of the relentless hemorrhage that had been silently sapping away the patient's life. The room seemed to hold its breath as Dr. Smithe delicately opened the area we had suspected, and there, in a visceral and haunting moment, blood began to pour out, revealing the devastating extent of the internal damage.

The patient had been battling severe internal bleeding since the auto accident, and the situation was far graver than we had initially comprehended. The liver, a vital organ, had sustained significant damage, and a critical decision loomed before us—we needed to resect a portion of it to staunch the relentless flow of blood.

At this critical juncture, our efforts to control the profuse bleeding and restore the damaged liver were conducted with a relentless sense of urgency. However, despite our relentless endeavors, the ominous flatline appeared on the cardiac monitor.

I recognized the imperative for decisive action. Without hesitation, I issued instructions to the attending nurse to retrieve the defibrillator machine. In that charged moment, the room itself seemed to collectively hold its breath as I delivered the vital and life-saving electrical shock, fervently willing the patient's faltering heart to respond and reignite the fragile spark of life.

Remarkably, the patient's heart rhythm was restored, and he came back to life. We returned to address the liver injury and successfully stem the internal bleeding. The surgery was far from over, but the immediate crisis had passed, and the patient had been given a second chance at life.

After several hours in the operating room, we managed to repair his trachea, allowing him to breathe without the pen, but I knew that the news I had to deliver to his wife would be devastating. the patient's vocal cords were irreparably damaged, leaving him with a profound loss—his voice. As I met with his wife, I saw the anguish in her eyes as I gently conveyed the difficult truth. The silence that followed was heavy with grief, and I could only offer my empathy and support during this trying time.

But the challenges didn't end there. After the surgery, the patient's abdomen remained tender and distended, raising concerns about further complications. Another CT scan was ordered, and it revealed the grim truth that he needed yet another surgery to address ongoing abdominal bleeding. The severity of the liver damage had taken its toll, and despite our best efforts, the bleeding was too extensive to control. As we prepared for the second surgery, we knew that the odds were stacked against us.

In the operating room once again, we faced an uphill battle. The patient's condition had become increasingly critical, and we were fighting against time. Despite our best efforts and the collective expertise of the surgical team, we were unable to save the patient. The internal bleeding had taken a toll on his already weakened body, and he ultimately succumbed on the operating table.

CHAPTER FOUR

THE HOCKEY GAME

THE TRANSITION from day to night shift at the ER had a way of casting a different light on the familiar hallways and bustling activity. It was my first night on the night shift, and the hospital seemed to take on an entirely new persona, one shrouded in shadows and punctuated by the stark, sterile glow of fluorescent lights. The night air carried a sense of quiet anticipation, as though it held the promise of secrets yet to be revealed.

As I settled into the rhythm of the night, the dimly lit emergency room hummed with a subdued energy. It was during those hushed hours when life often took unexpected turns. Just as I was beginning to acclimate to the quiet, the distant wails of sirens pierced the night, growing closer and more urgent with each passing second. An ambulance pulled into the bay, its crimson lights painting the surroundings in shades of emergency red. I braced myself for what lay ahead as the doors swung open, revealing the paramedics, their faces etched with concern, and a patient whose condition was far from ordinary.

Vincent, a man in the prime of his life, arrived on a gurney flanked by two anxious friends. It was immediately apparent that this was no ordinary case. As the paramedics provided a hurried briefing, I learned that the three of them had been on their way to celebrate Vincent's 30th birthday by attending a thrilling hockey game, a joyous occasion that had quickly transformed into a harrowing nightmare. Their evening had taken a devastating turn when their sleek limousine encountered an unforeseen patch of treacherous ice on the road, resulting in a horrific collision that had left all of them battered, bruised, and in urgent need of life-saving medical attention.

The pallor of uncertainty hung over the emergency room as we hastily assessed the patient's condition. His injuries were extensive, and it was evident that this was a race against time. A skull fracture, ominous and foreboding, loomed as a formidable challenge to his survival. It was a bleak prognosis, but we clung to a fragile thread of hope, determined to do everything within our power to tilt the scales in favor of life. the patient's friends, visibly shaken by the traumatic turn of events, stood by his side, a testament to the bonds of friendship that transcended even the darkest of hours.

The circumstances that had brought the patient into our emergency room were as sudden and chilling as the icy road that had led them here. At the epicenter of the ill-fated celebration, the patient bore the brunt of the tragic collision. The initial evaluation painted a dire picture, revealing a skull fracture of devastating proportions—a grim prognosis that cast a shadow of uncertainty over his very survival. It was a somber moment, standing on the precipice of the unknown, where the odds seemed overwhelmingly stacked against him.

The operating room, bathed in the sterile glow of surgical lights, became our battleground against the encroaching darkness of despair. The fractured skull, an emblem of the violent collision, demanded meticulous attention, and every movement of the surgical team was deliberate, driven by a fierce determination to save a life. In the midst of the complex and high-stakes procedure, the air was charged with tension, and the weight of responsibility hung heavily on our shoulders. The very essence of life and death seemed to dance on the edge of a surgeon's scalpel as we navigated the treacherous path toward the patient's recovery.

Inside the operating room, a sense of tension permeated the air, creating an atmosphere charged with gravity and anticipation. the patient's injuries were nothing short of catastrophic, and the surgery unfolding before us was a high-stakes gamble against the relentless march of time.

The fractured skull, a grim reminder of the collision's violence, commanded our undivided attention. Every member of the surgical team moved with deliberate precision, driven by an unwavering determination to tip the scales in favor of life. The sterile lights overhead cast a stark contrast on the glistening surgical instruments laid out with meticulous care, emphasizing the solemnity of our mission. The room echoed with the soft murmurs of focused communication and the rhythmic cadence of heart monitors.

However, as the surgery progressed, an unexpected and heart-wrenching complication arose. the patient began to bleed profusely, his vital signs plummeting in a distressing symphony of alarms. Panic threatened to consume us, but the years of training and experience that had brought us to this moment kicked in with unwavering resolve. In a matter of seconds that felt like an eternity, I called for everyone in the room to search for the elusive source of the bleeding, a desperate effort to stave off the looming specter of mortality.

It was Dr. Stanley, a respected member of the surgical team, who discovered the anomaly—a tear in the patient's renal artery, a critical conduit of life-sustaining blood supply. The discovery sent shockwaves through the room as we grappled with the implications of this hidden complication. With swift and skillful hands, Dr. Stanley stitched the tear in a bid to halt the hemorrhage and restore stability to our patient.

As the surgery to repair the patient's fractured skull and address his extensive injuries progressed, an unforeseen twist in the medical drama unfolded within the sterile confines of the operating room. Dr. Stanley, who was a skilled surgeon renowned for his expertise in stitching the more resilient tissues of the heart, was faced with the formidable challenge posed by the delicate nature of the renal artery. The meticulous stitch, executed with the best intentions, proved unable to withstand the unique demands of this intricate arterial repair. The consequences were devastating, setting off a chain reaction that plunged us deeper into the medical abyss.

Compounded by the trauma sustained during the accident, the patient's compromised bowel could no longer withstand the stresses imposed by the surgical intervention. The once-cohesive tissues yielded to the mounting pressure, leading to a tear in the bowel's delicate fabric. This breach unleashed a nightmarish cascade, permitting the escape of stool and digestive fluids into the sterile cavity of his abdomen. The specter of sepsis, a relentless and potentially life-threatening infection, loomed ominously, threatening to engulf the patient's already precarious state. Within the hushed and pressurized environment of the operating room, we found ourselves battling not only the consequences of the initial trauma but also a complex web of complications that demanded immediate and precise intervention.

I embarked on a mission to correct the complex web of complications that had arisen. In the wake of Dr. Stanley's efforts, our patient's life hung in the balance, and every action we took was a high-stakes gamble. We needed to address the torn bowel, staunch the seeping contamination, and navigate the treacherous path toward saving the patient's life.

Hours stretched into a relentless struggle as we toiled tirelessly to rectify the myriad of issues that had beset our patient. The operating room became a battleground, with surgeons, nurses, and medical equipment in a synchronized dance of urgency and precision. With unwavering determination, we managed to close the devastating tear and transitioned the patient to the Intensive Care Unit, where he lay in a stable yet precarious condition.

However, the relentless march of time and the complexities of the patient's injuries were not yet done testing our resolve. Within the span of a mere 24 hours, the ominous signs of deterioration began to emerge once more, casting a somber shadow over the fragile stability we had fought so hard to achieve. As the attending physician a gnawing suspicion tugged at the corners of my consciousness, prompting me to scrutinize the subtle yet unmistakable changes in the patient's condition. It was a gnawing intuition honed by years of experience, an unwavering sense that whispered of an impending crisis—a suspicion I could not afford to ignore.

Without hesitation, I made the call to rush the patient back into the unforgiving embrace of the operating room. My worst fears were realized as the surgical team embarked on the daunting task of reopening the surgical site. It was a pivotal moment, fraught with the haunting memories of our previous struggles. As the hours ticked away, every suture, every decision, was a delicate thread that wove the tapestry of the patient's fate.

Regrettably, despite our tireless efforts and unwavering dedication, the patient's condition deteriorated significantly. The surgery initially intended to rescue him, but unfortunately, became the arena where his final moments unfolded. On the operating table, his vital signs deteriorated to the point where resuscitation was unsuccessful, and he experienced a cardiac arrest.

CHAPTER FIVE

THE ENIGMA OF PATIENT X

AS A SEASONED MEDICAL PROFESSIONAL, I've had my fair share of hellish experiences in dealing with patients whose symptoms didn't at first seem to have any known medical explanation. Throughout the course of my career, I've come across rare medical anomalies more than a few times but I've never been a part of or gone through anything quite like what I went through with who my colleagues and I called "Patient X." Patient X first came to our attention when she was admitted into the emergency department at the hospital where I was working at the time, in 1986 in Chicago, Illinois. She was middle aged, and going forward I will refer to her as Mrs. Anderson, in the interest of protecting her anonymity and privilege as a patient.

Mrs. Anderson was a 45-year-old woman who, until

that fateful day, had enjoyed a relatively uneventful medical history. She had no prior major illnesses or surgeries, making her condition all the more perplexing. She presented with severe abdominal pain, fever, and an unmistakable air of distress. It wasn't long before her case became a topic of fascination and intrigue among the medical staff, and for good reason. Upon admission, our initial assessment revealed a fever of 101.4°F (38.6°C) and a heart rate that exceeded 100 beats per minute. The most striking finding, however, was the excruciating tenderness in her lower abdomen. The pain was so intense that even the lightest touch elicited grimaces of agony. Suspecting a possible infection, we promptly ordered a battery of diagnostic tests. Blood work revealed an elevated white blood cell count, pointing towards an active inflammatory process. A computed tomography (CT) scan of her abdomen was equally baffling. It showed signs of severe inflammation around her cecum and ascending colon, leading us to consider the possibility of acute appendicitis or diverticulitis. To confirm the diagnosis, we decided to proceed with an exploratory laparotomy—a surgical procedure in which we open the abdominal cavity to directly visualize and assess the affected area. This would also allow us to take any necessary therapeutic measures.

As I stood in the operating room, scalpel in hand, I

couldn't help but wonder what lay beneath the surface of Mrs. Anderson's abdominal cavity. Little did I know, the answer would turn this routine procedure into a medical mystery. Upon entering her abdominal cavity, I was met with a scene that defied explanation. Mrs. Anderson's cecum and ascending colon were indeed inflamed, as the CT scan had suggested, but there was something more—a structure that should not have been there. It appeared as if a small, sac-like organ had attached itself to her cecum, almost like a parasitic growth. This anomaly was unlike anything I had seen before in my career. We decided to proceed cautiously, fearing that this unexpected growth could be malignant or harboring infection. Carefully, I dissected the structure away from her colon, all the while wondering what it could be. The surgical specimen was sent to the pathology department for further examination. What came back from the pathologist left us even more perplexed. The structure was indeed a sac-like organ, resembling a tiny appendix, but it was filled with a thick, gelatinous substance that didn't resemble any normal tissue. Its appearance was eerie, almost extraterrestrial. Further analysis of the gelatinous substance revealed an astonishing revelation—it was composed of a substance akin to cerebrospinal fluid, the clear liquid that bathes the brain and spinal cord. This was utterly unprecedented in the world of medicine. An appendix-like structure filled with cerebrospinal fluid. It defied all known medical knowledge.

We conferred with specialists from various fields, including gastroenterology, surgery, and pathology. None could provide a definitive explanation for this bizarre anomaly. The cerebrospinal fluid within the sac-like structure contained no malignant cells, ruling out the possibility of cancer. There were no signs of infection either. With no concrete answers, we were left with a host of unanswered questions. How did this structure come to be? What function, if any, did it serve? And most perplexingly, how was it connected to Mrs. Anderson's acute abdominal pain and inflammation? We decided to delve deeper into the literature, hoping to find even a remote precedent for this peculiar condition. Hours turned into days, and days into weeks, as we scoured medical journals, textbooks, and online databases. It soon became evident that we were dealing with a medical anomaly so rare that it had never been documented in all of known written medical history. We consulted with experts from around the world, reaching out to colleagues and researchers who specialized in the most obscure and unusual medical conditions. Yet, nobody could shed light on the nature of Mrs. Anderson's condition. In the midst of this medical mystery,

Mrs. Anderson's health remained a top priority. Her recovery was slow, but with intensive medical management, including broad-spectrum antibiotics and pain control, her abdominal inflammation gradually subsided. We were able to discharge her from the hospital, but the enigma of her condition persisted.

After her discharge, we followed up with Mrs. Anderson regularly, monitoring her progress closely. Remarkably, she continued to improve, and her abdominal pain eventually disappeared. Yet, the unanswered questions lingered, haunting both the medical team and Mrs. Anderson herself. To better understand this perplexing case, we decided to conduct a series of follow-up tests and investigations. One of the key questions we sought to answer was whether the cerebrospinal fluid within the sac-like structure had any neurological properties or implications. We performed a lumbar puncture, commonly known as a spinal tap, to collect a sample of cerebrospinal fluid from Mrs. Anderson's spine. The results were astonishing. The cerebrospinal fluid extracted from her spine was a perfect match to the substance found within the sac-like structure in her abdomen. This connection only deepened the mystery. Further imaging studies, including magnetic resonance imaging (MRI) and positron emission tomography (PET) scans, were conducted to examine Mrs. Anderson's central nervous system. These tests revealed no abnormalities in her brain or spinal cord. Her neurological function remained entirely intact, and she reported no unusual sensations or symptoms. As we continued to explore this medical enigma, we began to consider the possibility of an embryological anomaly—a remnant of fetal development that had somehow persisted into adulthood. However, the anatomical location of the structure within her abdomen made this theory unlikely, as no known embryological structures matched its characteristics.

Another avenue of investigation involved a genetic analysis of Mrs. Anderson's DNA. We hoped that genetic testing might uncover a mutation or variation that could shed light on her condition. However, the genetic analysis returned no abnormalities or mutations that could explain the presence of the sac-like structure or the cerebrospinal fluid within it. With each test and consultation, we found ourselves delving deeper into uncharted territory. The medical anomaly of Patient X remained a baffling and unsolved riddle, defying the boundaries of our understanding of human physiology. Over time, Mrs. Anderson's health continued to improve, and she resumed her normal activities. The abdominal pain that had once plagued her had vanished completely. Yet, the specter of the mysterious sac-like structure and its bizarre contents remained in the background, an enduring reminder of the perplexing case that had baffled the medical community. Years passed, and Patient X gradually faded from the headlines of medical discussions. The anomaly of her condition remained unresolved, a testament to the boundless complexity of the human body and the limitations of medical science. As I reflect on the extraordinary journey of Patient X, I am reminded that medicine is as much about the questions we cannot answer as it is about the ones we can. The case of Mrs. Anderson stands as a testament to the uncharted territories that continue to exist within the field of medicine, waiting to be explored by future generations of healthcare professionals.

Though the enigma of Patient X remains unsolved, it serves as a humbling reminder of the vastness of the medical unknown. It is a reminder that, even in our age of advanced technology and scientific knowledge, there are still medical mysteries that defy explanation, challenging us to push the boundaries of our understanding and embrace the uncertainty that accompanies the practice of medicine. Despite this medical anomaly remaining a complete and total enigma to everyone who has ever come across it, it continued to challenge the limits of medical knowledge, pushing the boundaries of what was understood about human anatomy and physiology. While the answers remained elusive, the pursuit of knowledge and the dedication of countless medical professionals and researchers served as a testament to the unwavering commitment of the medical community to unravel the most perplexing of mysteries. Despite years of investigation, collaborative efforts, and advancements in medical science, the origins and significance of the sac-like structure filled with cerebrospinal fluid within her abdomen remain unknown. While the answers may remain elusive for now, the pursuit of knowledge and the quest for understanding continue, ensuring that the mystery of Patient X will remain a beacon of curiosity and intrigue for generations of medical professionals to come.

The ongoing quest to decipher the enigma of Patient X's condition has not been without its challenges. It has required a level of dedication and collaboration rarely seen in the medical field. The case has drawn together experts from diverse disciplines, fostering an environment where innovation and unconventional thinking are embraced. One of the more recent breakthroughs in our understanding of Patient X's condition came from an unexpected source—computational modeling. A team of computational biologists and bioinformaticians decided to approach the problem from a different angle. They developed intricate computer simulations to model the behavior of the sac-like structure and its interaction with nearby tissues. The simulations revealed a fascinating phenomenon. The structure appeared to pulsate rhythmically, generating subtle waves that radiated outward. This pulsation was not due to muscle contractions but rather seemed to be driven by fluid dynamics within the sac-like organ. The team theorized that the rhythmic pulsation might have a functional purpose. Could it be related to the transport of cerebrospinal-like fluid, or was it something entirely different? This revelation sparked a new wave of experimental investigations. Further imaging studies were conducted with a specific focus on capturing the pulsation of the structure. High-speed imaging and advanced MRI techniques allowed researchers to visualize the phenomenon in unprecedented detail. It became clear that the rhythmic pulsation was not isolated to the sac-like structure alone— it extended into the surrounding tissues, creating a dynamic network of fluid movement. This observation led to a groundbreaking hypothesis—that the sac-like structure might serve as a reservoir for cerebrospinal-like fluid, redistributing it to various parts of the body in a regulated manner. It was a theory that challenged conventional wisdom, as cerebrospinal fluid was traditionally associated exclusively with the central nervous system.

To test this hypothesis, researchers initiated a series of experiments to measure cerebrospinal-like fluid levels in different areas of Mrs. Anderson's body. What they discovered was nothing short of astounding. Not only did the fluid levels within the sac-like structure fluctuate, but they also correlated with Mrs. Anderson's physiological state. During moments of stress or heightened activity, the fluid within the sac-like structure seemed to increase, providing a surge of cerebrospinal-like fluid to the surrounding tissues. This finding suggested a dynamic and adaptive role for the structure in response to the body's needs. The implications of this discovery were profound. It hinted at the possibility of a previously unknown regulatory system within the human body—one that involved the transport and redistribution of cerebrospinal-like fluid outside the central nervous system. The sac-like structure, once regarded as an anomaly, now appeared to play a vital role in maintaining physiological balance. As the medical community delved deeper into the functional aspects of the sac-like structure, another revelation emerged. The genetic markers associated with neural development within the sac-like organ seemed to be active, albeit in a unique and specialized manner. They were involved in the regulation of fluid dynamics and the maintenance of tissue homeostasis. This finding challenged our understanding of gene expression and function. It suggested that genes traditionally associated with neural development could have broader roles in tissue regulation and adaptation. It opened up new avenues of research and inquiry, sparking excitement and curiosity within the scientific community.

The journey to uncover the mysteries of Patient X's condition was far from over, but the recent breakthroughs had reinvigorated the quest for answers. The medical community, fueled by a newfound sense of purpose and possibility, redoubled its efforts to understand the full extent of the sac-like structure's role in the human body. Patient X, once a symbol of perplexity and uncertainty, now stood at the center of a medical revolution. Her unique condition had led to the discovery of a previously unknown regulatory system within the human body, challenging long-held assumptions and inspiring a new era of medical exploration. The story of Patient X says a lot, in my opinion, about the boundless capacity for discovery within the field of medicine. It demonstrates the power of curiosity, collaboration, and innovation in unraveling the most enigmatic of medical mysteries. Patient X's journey continues to inspire not only the medical community but also individuals around the world who are captivated by the resilience of the human spirit and the unwavering commitment to seek answers, no matter how elusive they may seem. As we look to the future, we can only imagine the discoveries that await us as we explore the frontiers of human health and disease, one enigma at a time.

CHAPTER SIX

SENSE OF DUTY

MY DEPLOYMENT as an Army Medic had been a demanding journey spanning three arduous years. The constant rotations through combat zones, countless medical emergencies, and the unwavering commitment to serving my country had left me yearning for the day when I would finally return home. That day had arrived, and as I stood in the bustling airport terminal, it felt like a surreal dream, a moment I had eagerly awaited but could hardly believe had come.

The airport, a world within itself, teemed with travelers from all walks of life. Each person carried their unique stories and destinations, blending into a vibrant tapestry of human experiences. It was a vivid reminder of the diversity and interconnectedness of our world, a contrast to the often isolated and intense environment of my deployment.

With a few hours to spare before my flight, I decided to ease into my vacation by stopping at a nearby bar. It was a moment to unwind, to let go of the stresses and responsibilities of my military service, and to savor the freedom that awaited me at home. The camaraderie of fellow travelers filled the air, their conversations and laughter creating a sense of community in the midst of the transient nature of air travel. As I ordered a drink and listened to the tales of those around me, memories of my deployment surfaced – the challenges, the camaraderie, and the bonds forged under the crucible of duty.

In preparation for the flight, I picked up some gum to handle the inevitable pressure changes during the journey and a bottle of water to stay hydrated. These small, habitual gestures were remnants of the discipline instilled by years of military service – always prepared, always vigilant.

As I stepped onto the plane, my senses were immediately overwhelmed by the familiar sights and sounds. The aircraft was a microcosm of my world, filled with returning soldiers who, like me, had endured the trials of the Gulf War. We were a diverse group, representing different branches of the military, various ranks, and a wide range of specialties, but in that moment, we were all united by a shared mission – the mission to return home.

Amid the bustle of boarding, we exchanged nods, smiles, and knowing glances, recognizing the unspoken bond that connected us. Some wore the physical scars of battle, while others carried the weight of memories that only those who had served could truly understand. We had all experienced the grueling demands of deployment. Now, as we settled into our seats, we were on the cusp of a different kind of journey.

For me, being an Army Medic had been a calling, a role that demanded the ability to remain calm in the face of chaos. I had been deployed to various combat zones, from the scorching deserts of the Middle East to the rugged terrain of Afghanistan. My days were filled with treating wounded soldiers, providing medical support in field hospitals, and witnessing the harsh realities of war. I had seen the resilience of the human spirit in the face of adversity, and I had also seen the devastating toll that conflict could exact on both body and soul.

Before we could even take off, I laid my head back against my headrest and, thanks to the shot of tequila, I fell asleep. Exhaustion had overtaken my soul.

We were probably about one hour into the flight and a flight attendant gently tapped me on the shoulder. I was startled awake. Just as my eyes opened a clap of thunder surrounded the cabin. We were flying through a severe storm. The thunder and lightning that surrounded the plane reminded me of being in combat. My heart was racing. The flight attendant gently whispered to me that I was needed. There was a soldier in the back who needed urgent care.

Amidst the controlled commotion, I followed the flight attendant's lead, my anticipation heightened by the ominous storm that encircled our aircraft. The relentless flicker of lightning transformed the exterior into an unpredictable battleground, reminiscent of projectiles fired in the dark abyss of the sky.

Without hesitation, I followed the flight attendant to the rear of the plane, my training and instinct taking over. The scene that greeted me was all too familiar – a soldier, pale and in visible pain, required immediate medical attention. I introduced myself and swiftly assessed the situation, recognizing the urgency of the soldier's deteriorating condition.

Working alongside the flight attendants, we created a makeshift medical area at the back of the plane. My medical kit, a trusted companion throughout my deployment, became a lifeline as I performed a series of tests and examinations to determine the soldier's condition. The cabin crew and passengers offered their support, their concern and gratitude apparent.

Amidst the tumultuous atmosphere of the plane, I swiftly approached the soldier in distress. He lay sprawled on the floor, gasping for breath, his chest rising and falling with great effort. The urgency of the situation was palpable as I knelt down beside him, my training and experience guiding my every movement. It was a critical moment that demanded rapid assessment and decisive action.

As I began my examination, a troubling observation emerged. I listened intently, my stethoscope pressed against his chest, but there was an ominous absence of breath sounds emanating from one side of his chest. It was a chilling confirmation of what I had feared - a collapsed lung, a condition that warranted immediate attention. Time was of the essence, and I knew that the soldier's life depended on swift and expert medical intervention. With a sense of urgency that matched the gravity of the situation, I communicated the imperative need to get him to a hospital as quickly as possible, recognizing that his journey home had taken an unforeseen and perilous turn.

Time hung in the balance, an ever-tightening noose around the soldier's struggling breath. With each passing moment, the gravity of the situation became increasingly apparent. It was abundantly clear that the soldier's life hung in the balance, and the prospect of making it to a hospital in time grew dim. Faced with the reality that there was no alternative, I turned to the flight attendant, my voice firm and determined, requesting napkins and lighter to illuminate the impending procedure.

With a sense of resolve, I reached for my meticulously organized medical bag, every tool and instrument a lifeline in this critical moment. As I palpated between the soldier's ribs, his eyes fixed on mine, a silent understanding passed between us. He knew the gravity of the situation, the necessity of the imminent procedure. I urgently requested as much ice as possible, preparing to numb the area between the ribs, the first crucial step in a life-saving maneuver. With the flight attendant's assistance, we packed the soldier's side in ice, numbing him as much as I could.

I began the delicate procedure of inserting the chest tube, a critical lifeline in our high-altitude medical drama. The soldier's face once contorted in agony, now bore a stoic determination as he braced himself for what lay ahead. The dim cabin lighting cast shadows that danced across his features, emphasizing the tension etched in his furrowed brow. His eyes remained locked onto mine; a silent pact forged in the crucible of this life-or-death moment.

As I prepared to make the incision, I couldn't help but notice the flight attendant, standing by with a mixture of fear and resolve etched across her face. The gravity of the situation had taken its toll, and she teetered on the edge of consciousness, a testament to the harrowing nature of our mid-air medical emergency. Her presence was a reminder of the stakes involved, the thin line between life and tragedy that we were navigating.

Remarkably, throughout the entire procedure, the soldier did not cry out in pain. His unwavering resolve and trust in my expertise resonated throughout the cabin. The room was filled with a visible tension, as everyone held their collective breath. And then, as the chest tube found its mark, relief washed over the back of the plane like a tidal wave. The soldier's breathing, once labored and strained, began to stabilize. The trapped air was released, and the collapsed lung gradually started to re-expand, proof of the life-saving measures undertaken in the heart of the storm.

It became clear that the soldier's condition was critical, and we urgently needed to make an emergency landing to provide the proper medical care. I relayed this information to the flight crew, who quickly coordinated with air traffic control to reroute our flight to the nearest airport.

As the plane descended and touched down on an unfamiliar runway, the atmosphere inside the cabin grew tense. Every passenger understood the gravity of the situation, and the soldier's life hung in the balance. Waiting for us was a team of medical professionals and emergency responders who swiftly transported the soldier to a nearby hospital.

With a surgeon's precision, I began the delicate procedure of inserting the chest tube, a critical lifeline in our high-altitude medical drama. The soldier's face once contorted in agony, now bore a stoic determination as he braced himself for what lay ahead. The cabin lighting cast shadows that danced across his features, emphasizing the tension etched in his furrowed brow. His eyes remained locked onto mine; a silent pact forged in the crucible of this life-or-death moment.

As I prepared to make the incision, I couldn't help but notice the flight attendant, standing by with a mixture of fear and resolve etched across her face. The gravity of the situation had taken its toll, and she teetered on the edge of consciousness, a testament to the harrowing nature of our mid-air medical emergency.

Remarkably, throughout the entire procedure, the soldier did not cry out in pain. His unwavering resolve and trust in my expertise resonated throughout the cabin. The room was filled with a tension you could taste, as everyone on that plane held their collective breath, hoping for a miracle at 30,000 feet. And then, as the chest tube found its mark, relief washed over us like a tidal wave. The soldier's breathing, once labored and strained, began to stabilize. The trapped air was released, and the collapsed lung gradually started to re-expand, a testament to the life-saving measures undertaken in the heart of the storm.

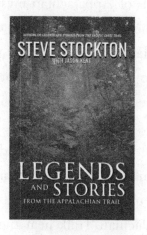

MISSING PEOPLE CASES

Over the years, several hikers and individuals have gone
missing while venturing on or around the Appalachian

Trail. While many missing persons cases are eventually resolved as lost hikers are found or their fates are discovered, others remain shrouded in mystery, contributing to the trail's lore and history. Below are some of the most well-known or intriguing cases.

Vanishing Echoes: The Dennis Lloyd Martin Disappearance

In the annals of Appalachian mysteries, few are as enduring and heartbreaking as the disappearance of Dennis Lloyd Martin. In 1969, the six-year-old vanished without a trace from the Great Smoky Mountains National Park, leaving behind a trail of questions and a legacy of sorrow.

June 14, 1969, started as a joyous day for the Martin family. On a camping trip in the Smokies, the family decided to hike up to Spence Field, a popular meadow along the Appalachian Trail, near the border between North Carolina and Tennessee. Upon reaching the destination, Dennis and his brother, along with some other children, decided to play a prank on the adults by jumping out of the bushes to surprise them.

The boys were supposed to jump out of the bushes simultaneously to surprise the adults. While the other boys executed the plan, Dennis, who had been seen going behind a bush, did not reappear. This marked the last time anyone saw him. Despite wearing a highly visible, bright red shirt, he seemed to have vanished into thin air.

Dennis's father, William Martin, immediately sprung into action, searching a two-mile radius around Spence Field but to no avail. Soon after, the National Park Service was notified, and one of the most extensive search-and-rescue missions in the history of the southeastern United States began.

The search for Dennis was plagued by a series of challenges. Heavy rains fell in the area soon after his disappearance, washing away potential tracks and clues. Additionally, there were communication issues and coordination problems among the different agencies and hundreds of volunteers involved in the search.

During the search, a family reported hearing a child's scream and later finding shoe prints consistent with a boy's Oxford-style shoe, which Dennis was wearing. Unfortunately, this lead was not immediately followed up on, leading to speculation and controversy regarding the investigation's handling.

Over the years, theories about Dennis's disappearance have proliferated. Some believe he was abducted; others think he succumbed to the elements, while others speculate about wild animal attacks.

The disappearance of Dennis Lloyd Martin has left an indelible mark on the Great Smoky Mountains National Park and the broader Appalachian community. The case has spawned countless articles, documentaries, and book chapters, serving as a chilling reminder of the wilderness's unpredictability and danger.

Despite the passage of over five decades, the mystery of Dennis Lloyd Martin's disappearance remains unsolved, casting a long, enigmatic shadow over the Smokies. The story continues to evoke a sense of loss and caution in those who venture into the vast, beautiful, and sometimes unforgiving expanse of the Appalachian wilderness. Each retelling of the tale serves not only as a eulogy for a life lost too soon but also as a solemn reminder to respect and navigate carefully through nature's mesmerizing but perilous terrains.

Vanished in the Vales: The Disappearance of Thelma Pauline Melton

In the realm of mysterious disappearances along the Appalachian Trail, the case of Thelma Pauline Melton, affectionately known as "Polly," stands out as one of the most haunting and puzzling. The story of her disappearance in 1981 remains etched in the collective memory of the hiking community and those familiar with the Great Smoky Mountains National Park.

At the age of 58, Thelma Pauline Melton was an experienced hiker, intimately acquainted with the undulating trails and picturesque vistas of the Smokies. She often retreated to the embrace of these ancient hills, seeking solace and rejuvenation amidst their silent strength and timeless beauty.

On September 25, 1981, Polly set out with friends on what was supposed to be a serene and invigorating hike near the Appalachian Trail in the Deep Creek area of the park. Engulfed by a canvas of lush greenery and accompanied by the melodic whispers of the creek, the group of friends was unaware that the day would unfold into a haunting tale of mystery and loss.

Polly was walking ahead of her two friends, and as the trail unfolded, she moved out of their sight. It was the last time her companions, and indeed anyone, would see her. When her friends arrived at the designated meeting point, Polly was nowhere to be found. The tranquil ambiance of the park swiftly transformed into an ominous silence, heavy with the weight of the unknown.

The news of Polly's disappearance sent shockwaves through the community, prompting an immediate and extensive search. Hundreds of volunteers, park rangers, and law enforcement personnel combed through the rugged terrain, plunging into the dense foliage and navigating the treacherous landscape in a race against time.

Despite the exhaustive efforts and the eyes meticulously scanning every inch of the area, no trace of Polly was found. The search expanded, covering a broad swath of land, but the Smokies remained silent, guarding their secrets with stoic resolve.

In the wake of Polly's disappearance, various theories and speculations swirled around, attempting to make sense of the inexplicable. Some believed she might have lost her footing and fallen into a concealed ravine or crevice, while others speculated about possible foul play. However, with no evidence or leads emerging, the case gradually grew cold, leaving a void filled by whispers, stories, and the undying hope for closure.

Polly's disappearance remains one of the many mysteries that cloak the Appalachian Trail and the Smokies. Over the years, her story has been revisited by journalists, investigators, and those intrigued by unsolved cases. Yet, the answers remain elusive, tucked away in the silent heart of the mountains.

For those who tread upon the trails that Polly once walked, her story serves as a sobering reminder of the unpredictability and inherent dangers of the wild. It's a tale whispered through the rustling leaves and echoed in the murmuring creeks, a silent hymn to the enigmatic and indomitable spirit of the Appalachian wilderness.

The disappearance of Thelma Pauline Melton is a haunting narrative that continues to reverberate through the corridors of time. It's a poignant reminder of the mysteries that unfold in the shadows of nature's grandeur, the tales spun in the silence of the forests, and the echoes of the lost that blend with the eternal symphony of the wild. Each step on the Appalachian Trail whispers these stories, inviting those who listen to reflect, remember, and tread lightly upon the sacred tapestry of earth and sky.

Lost in the Wilderness: The Geraldine Largay Story

Introduction

Geraldine Largay, affectionately known as "Gerry"

to friends and "Inchworm" to her fellow hikers, was a 66-year-old experienced hiker from Tennessee who met a tragic fate on the Appalachian Trail in 2013. Her disappearance and the subsequent discovery of her remains are sober reminders of the unpredictable nature of wilderness adventures.

Geraldine began her thru-hike of the Appalachian Trail in April 2013 with a close friend. They planned to traverse the approximately 2,200-mile-long trail from Georgia to Maine together. However, due to a family emergency, her companion had to leave the hike in June. Despite this, Geraldine decided to continue the journey solo, a decision that was supported by her husband, who would meet her at different sections of the trail to resupply.

On July 22, 2013, Geraldine sent a text to her husband, informing him of her plans to meet him in the town of Stratton, Maine, in a couple of days. This was the last communication anyone received from her. When she failed to appear at the designated location, concerns for her safety grew, initiating a massive search operation.

The search for Geraldine Largay was one of the largest in the history of the state of Maine. It involved multiple agencies, including the Maine Warden Service, the FBI, and numerous volunteers. Despite the extensive efforts, the search teams were unable to locate her, and as days turned into weeks and then months, hope of finding her alive dwindled.

Almost two years after her disappearance, on October 14, 2015, a surveyor working for the U.S. Navy found Geraldine's remains more than two miles away from the trail in a dense, wooded area. Her campsite indicated that she had survived for weeks after getting lost. Her journal entries, found at the site, revealed that she tried to reach her husband via text messages but without success due to the lack of cellular reception.

The discovery of Geraldine's remains brought a tragic conclusion to the mystery of her disappearance. The story highlighted the risks associated with solo hiking and the challenges of navigating the dense and often confusing terrain of the Appalachian Trail. Geraldine's fate is a stark reminder for all wilderness enthusiasts to take precautions, plan carefully, and always be prepared for the uncertainties of nature.

Geraldine Largay's story has since served as a cautionary tale within the hiking and outdoor adventure communities. It underscores the importance of preparation, the understanding of navigation tools, and the awareness of the environment in which one is traveling. Her journey and tragic end continue to resonate with those who tread the paths of the Appalachian Trail, serving as silent testimony to the awe-inspiring yet unforgiving wilderness that adventurers navigate.

The story of Geraldine "Inchworm" Largay is one of inspiration, adventure, and tragedy interwoven. While her spirit and passion for hiking continue to inspire, her unfortunate demise stands as a somber reminder of the respect and preparedness that the great outdoors demands. As hikers continue to traverse the undulating terrains and misty peaks of the Appalachian Trail, the tale of Geraldine Largay whispers through the trees, urging caution and reverence for the wild, unpredictable beauty of nature.

The Unseen Departure: Michael Hearon (2008)

Michael Hearon, whose disappearance in 2008 near the Appalachian Trail remains unresolved, has since been embedded in the complex tapestry of mysterious occurrences associated with the Great Smoky Mountains. This chapter seeks to shed light on the known details of his case, acknowledging the pain and uncertainty experienced by his family and friends.

Michael Hearon was a 51-year-old man from Blount

County, Tennessee, known for his affable nature and familiarity with the local terrains. An avid outdoorsman, Hearon was accustomed to the challenging landscapes of the Appalachian region.

On August 23, 2008, Hearon reportedly left his home, driving his 2004 Jeep Wrangler. He was headed towards his family's property in the Happy Valley area, a region near the Great Smoky Mountains National Park. Michael was wearing a black t-shirt, blue jeans, and tennis shoes. After he failed to return home, a search commenced to locate him, unfolding into a saga of mystery and uncertainty.

Hearon's Jeep was discovered on his family's property, with no signs of struggle or foul play. The vehicle was parked properly, and his keys were missing. It appeared as though Hearon had arrived at his destination but subsequently vanished without a trace.

Upon discovering the vehicle, local law enforcement and search-and-rescue teams initiated a comprehensive search operation. The extensive effort involved ground searches, canine units, and aerial surveys of the densely wooded area. Despite the meticulous and thorough search spanning weeks, no conclusive evidence or traces of Hearon were found, deepening the enigma of his disappearance.

In the wake of the unsuccessful search, various theories and speculations emerged. Some believed Hearon might have encountered a dangerous animal or fell victim to the treacherous terrains, while others considered the possibility of amnesia or intentional disappearance. However, without concrete evidence, all these remained mere speculations, leaving the case shrouded in uncertainty.

Michael Hearon's disappearance had a profound impact on his family and the local community. The lack of closure and answers left a void, with family members grappling with the unknown fate of their loved one. Over the years, the case has periodically resurfaced in local media, often reigniting interest and discussion among those familiar with the region and its mysteries.

The tale of Michael Hearon is a somber reminder of the mysteries held within the embrace of the majestic, yet unforgiving, Appalachian landscape. For the most accurate and current information, please refer to the latest resources and investigation updates.

The Unsolved Mystery of Paul David Braxton

Paul David Braxton's disappearance in 1988 near the Appalachian Trail remains one of the many unsolved mysteries associated with the Great Smoky

Mountains National Park. Despite the passage of time, the circumstances surrounding his vanishing continue to perplex and sadden those who learn of his story.

In 1988, Paul David Braxton, a native of North Carolina, went missing without a trace. His vehicle was found abandoned near a trailhead in the Great Smoky Mountains National Park, a vast expanse of wilderness that encompasses a portion of the Appalachian Trail.

The discovery of Braxton's car near the trailhead raised immediate concern, prompting search and rescue teams to comb the rugged terrain, dense forests, and hidden valleys of the park. Despite their meticulous and exhaustive efforts, no trace of Braxton was ever found, leaving family, friends, and the wider community puzzled and heartbroken.

Search efforts for Braxton were extensive, involving local law enforcement, park rangers, and volunteers. The challenging and often treacherous landscape of the Great Smoky Mountains presented significant obstacles, with search teams navigating steep cliffs, dense foliage, and fast-flowing rivers.

Days turned into weeks, and weeks into months, with each passing moment dimming the hope of finding Braxton alive. The search teams were relentless, but the vast and wild nature of the park swallowed all traces of him, leaving behind only questions and speculation.

Over the years, various theories have emerged regarding Braxton's disappearance. Some believe he may have fallen victim to an accident in the wilderness, perhaps losing his footing and falling into a ravine or being swept away by a river's strong currents. Others speculate that he might have encountered a wild animal or perhaps even foul play.

However, without evidence or concrete leads, these theories remain speculative. The absence of definitive answers has led to Braxton's story becoming part of the tapestry of legends and mysteries associated with the Appalachian Trail and the Great Smoky Mountains.

Braxton's disappearance had a profound impact on the local community and those who hike and treasure the Appalachian Trail. It served as a somber reminder of the unpredictability and inherent dangers of the wilderness. For those who knew him, his vanishing left a void that could never be filled, a wound that time could only partially heal.

The disappearance of Paul David Braxton in 1988 is a haunting and unsolved mystery that continues to echo through the valleys and over the peaks of the Great Smoky Mountains. His story is a testament to the allure and danger of the wild, a silent and unresolved melody that adds to the symphony of tales and legends born from the Appalachian Trail's misty paths. Each hiker who traverses these trails carries with them the stories of those who came before, including the unresolved and haunting tale of Paul David Braxton.

LEGENDS AND STORIES: FROM THE APPALACHIAN TRAIL

TUSKEGEE SYPHILIS EXPERIMENT

The Tuskegee Syphilis Experiment, also known as the Tuskegee Study of Untreated Syphilis in the Negro Male, is one of the most infamous cases of unethical human experimentation in U.S. history, and at one time was considered a conspiracy theory. The study was initially supposed to last six months but ended up continuing for 40 years, from 1932 to 1972.

ORIGINS:

The study began in 1932 in Macon County, Alabama, and was conducted by the U.S. Public Health Service (USPHS).

Dr. Taliaferro Clark was the original architect of the study. Initially, Dr. Clark intended the study to be a short-term project to record the progression of syphilis and then offer treatment. However, under subsequent leadership, the study's purpose shifted to observing the long-term effects of untreated syphilis.

KEY FIGURES / INSTITUTIONS OVER THE YEARS:

The initiation and continuation of the Tuskegee Syphilis Experiment were facilitated by a combination of institutional decisions by the USPHS, complicit actions by key individuals, and the broader societal context of racial discrimination and unequal access to healthcare. The study's prolonged duration, despite clear ethical violations, is a testament to the systemic issues that allowed such an experiment to persist for four decades.

- **Dr. Raymond Vonderlehr**: He succeeded Dr. Clark and became the on-site director of the study. Under his leadership, the intention of the study was redefined to observe untreated syphilis in black males until their deaths. Vonderlehr developed the procedures for the study and was involved in its operations for many years.
- **Dr. John Heller**: He was another central figure in the study who directed it for a significant portion of its duration, particularly during the years after World War II. Under his tenure, the withholding of treatment continued, even after penicillin was recognized as a standard and effective treatment for syphilis.
- **Dr. Oliver Wenger**: While not directly overseeing the study, Wenger was a key figure in the USPHS's venereal disease

section and supported the Tuskegee
experiment.

- **Tuskegee Institute**: The Tuskegee
Institute (now Tuskegee University), a
historically black college in Alabama, played
a role in the study. The USPHS
collaborated with the Institute, which
provided logistical support and helped gain
the trust of the local community. However,
it's essential to note that the primary
responsibility and decision-making authority
for the study's design and continuation lay
with the USPHS.

- **Dr. Eugene Dibble**: He was the head of
the John Andrew Hospital at the Tuskegee
Institute and was involved in the study,
mainly in its early stages.

- **Eunice Rivers**: She was a black nurse
who played a significant role in the day-to-
day operations of the study. Rivers was
responsible for maintaining contact with the
participants, ensuring they attended
scheduled appointments, and acted as a
bridge between the researchers and the
community. Because of her involvement and

trust within the community, many
participants stayed in the study.

MAIN FEATURES OF THE EXPERIMENT:

The study involved 600 black men, of which 399
had syphilis and 201 did not. The men were told they
were being treated for "bad blood," a colloquial term
used in the community to describe several ailments,
including syphilis, anemia, and fatigue.

The participants were not informed of their syphilis
diagnosis nor were they informed about the study's true
purpose. Instead, they were told they were receiving free
healthcare, meals, and burial insurance in exchange for
participating.

Even when penicillin became the standard treatment for syphilis in 1947, the men in the study were
neither informed about this development nor provided
with the antibiotic. Researchers intentionally withheld
treatment to observe the disease's progression.

DECEPTION:

There's no documented evidence that the men in the
Tuskegee Syphilis Experiment were collectively aware
that they were being deceived and subsequently made

public claims about the study during its early years or even much of its duration. It's essential to understand the context and the level of manipulation involved:

The participants were deceived from the start. They were told that they were being treated for "bad blood," a local term that could refer to several conditions, including syphilis, anemia, and fatigue. The U.S. Public Health Service provided them with placebos, ineffective methods, and diagnostic procedures under the guise of "treatment." Because of this, many of the men believed they were receiving genuine healthcare.

Medical authorities, especially during the time when the study began, were highly respected. The men had little reason to doubt the intentions of the health professionals involved, especially when they were provided with certain benefits like free medical check-ups and meals during examinations.

Nurse Rivers played a pivotal role in maintaining the trust of the participants. As a Black nurse who was part of their community, she was instrumental in keeping the men involved in the study. Her relationship with the participants further ensured that they felt they were in good hands.

Many of the participants were not well-informed about syphilis, its treatments, or the broader implications of medical research. This lack of information, combined with the intentional deception by the study's conductors, made it less likely for the men to question the proceedings.

The racial dynamics of the American South in the early to mid-20th century meant that Black individuals often faced systemic racism, were marginalized, and lacked resources. Such a context might have made it even more challenging for the participants to voice concerns or seek second opinions.

EXPOSED:

The Tuskegee Syphilis Experiment became public knowledge in 1972. The unethical practices of the study were brought to national attention by Peter Buxtun, a former Public Health Service interviewer and whistle-blower. Buxtun had expressed his concerns about the study to his superiors within the USPHS several times since the late 1960s, but it was only after no internal action was taken that he decided to go to the press.

Jean Heller, a reporter for the Associated Press, broke the story on July 25, 1972, revealing the details of the study to the general public. The article described how for four decades, the U.S. Public Health Service had deliberately withheld treatment from hundreds of black men with syphilis as part of a research experiment.

When the Tuskegee Syphilis Experiment was

exposed by Jean Heller in 1972, the government did not deny the study's existence or its details. The facts were well-documented, and Peter Buxtun, the whistleblower, provided evidence about the experiment. Additionally, the U.S. Public Health Service, which had overseen the study, did not dispute the revelations once they were made public and shut it down.

However, in the immediate aftermath of the story breaking, some officials and representatives of the U.S. Public Health Service tried to justify or defend the study's intent and procedures, citing the research's importance or arguing that standards and norms had changed since the study began in 1932. This stance was not a denial but rather an attempt to provide context or justification, which was widely seen as insufficient and unsatisfactory given the gross ethical violations.

The media, for its part, generally reported on the story with shock and outrage. The revelations led to extensive media coverage, which played a crucial role in informing the public about the study's details and the ethical issues at stake.

The overwhelming negative reaction from the public, medical community, and media alike led to congressional hearings, which culminated in a stronger framework for the protection of human subjects in research studies and ultimately the creation of institutional review boards (IRBs) to oversee and approve research involving human participants.

CONSEQUENCES AND OUTCOMES:

Many participants of the study suffered severe health complications due to untreated syphilis, and some even died from the disease. Their families also suffered, with spouses becoming infected and children born with congenital syphilis.

In 1973, a $10 million out-of-court settlement was reached, and the U.S. government promised to give lifetime medical benefits and burial services to all living participants. The widows of the participants were also provided with health benefits.

In 1997, President Bill Clinton formally apologized on behalf of the U.S. government to the surviving participants of the study and their families.

The experiment sowed deep distrust among many in the Black community towards the U.S. healthcare system, which still reverberates today.

CONSPIRACY THEORIES THAT WERE TRUE

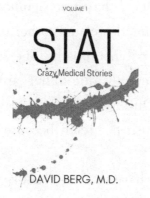

VOLUME 1

STAT

Crazy Medical Stories

DAVID BERG, M.D.

BRUSH YOUR TEETH

As a dental nurse, I've seen my fair share of rotten teeth and oral health issues, but let me tell you about the strangest case I've encountered so far.

We had an entry exam scheduled for a new patient, a woman in her forties. During the anamnesis, when we ask about the patient's main concerns, she simply wrote "tartar." I was taken aback, and even the doctor was puzzled. I mean, her panoramic X-ray (OPG) revealed a host of other dental problems, and yet she wanted us to focus on tartar first? It didn't quite add up. I was relatively new to the office at the time, but even I could tell that her OPG indicated a number of issues that needed attention. Nonetheless, she arrived for her appointment, and the doctor began discussing her case with her.

As it turns out, the most significant problem she faced was not directly related to her teeth but rather a condition called polyneuropathy. She had been hospitalized for several months due to her "arms and legs stopping working." During her hospital stay, she had to rely on nurses to brush her teeth because her hands were immobile.

So, here we have the tartar issue, which she could easily see for herself. The doctor instructed her to look at her lower frontal teeth. Now, picture this: a continuous layer of tartar extended from the back of her frontal teeth all the way down to the bottom of her tongue, spanning about 1 cm in length. I couldn't fathom the neglect her teeth must have endured during those months in the hospital for such an accumulation to occur. The tartar had caused severe localized periodontitis, to the extent that it was the only thing keeping her teeth from falling out. It was clear that the infection stemming from this issue was negatively impacting her overall health.

Thus, we had to prioritize cleaning out the tartar to the extent that the affected teeth could be extracted. This was necessary to eliminate the source of infection and promote her overall well-being. The treatment involved multiple tooth extractions, around six deep-cleaning dental hygiene sessions, several tooth fillings, and the provision of partial dentures. It was a lengthy and challenging process, but the patient worked hard alongside us.

Eventually, her condition improved significantly. She not only regained her dental health but also experienced a positive transformation in her overall well-being. From the dire state she was in when she first walked into our office, she gradually progressed to regular check-ups without any further problems. It was truly remarkable to witness the journey of her recovery.

This case served as a stark reminder of the importance of dental hygiene, especially for patients with compromised health conditions. It also highlighted the incredible impact that proper dental care can have on a person's overall health and quality of life. Despite the initial confusion surrounding her focus on tartar, it became clear that addressing that issue was a crucial step in restoring her dental and overall well-being.

I'm grateful to have been a part of her journey toward better oral health, and I hope her story serves as a testament to the transformative power of dedicated dental care.

STAT: CRAZY MEDICAL STORIES, VOLUME 1

CHAPTER SEVEN

THE MAN WHO GLOWED IN THE DARK

I'VE BEEN PRACTICING medicine for a long time and I've been thinking lately about writing a book about some of the more strange and mysterious medical anomalies I've come across and worked through in that time. As I went through the long list of odd and strange things I've seen throughout my decades of experience as a primary care physician, there's one case that sticks out in my mind more so than any of the others. This one case was a real test for me and at times made me think that it was all for nothing. However, with the help of several other professionals in the medical field, I eventually reached a conclusion and got the patient the help he so desperately needed. It's a good thing too because for a while I really considered that I might have to go back to school and start again, mainly due to the fact that I simply couldn't come up with the answers for this poor man. Well, I'm getting ahead of myself. Let me explain. Before I do I will say that I still must honor the doctor and patient privilege of privacy and therefore will be referring to my patient as only John throughout this story. John's case left an indelible mark on my life and opened my mind, and it forever altered my perspective on the complexity of the human body.

John was in his late twenties when he first walked into our clinic. I remember the day vividly - it was a rainy autumn morning, and the rain and wind beat against the windows, but the sun was still casting a warm glow on the reception area. John appeared nervous but determined, his eyes darting around the room as if he were searching for answers that had eluded him for years. John's chief complaint was unlike anything I had ever heard before. He explained that his body emitted a faint, otherworldly glow, visible only in the darkest of surroundings. Intrigued and skeptical in equal measure, I decided to delve deeper into his history to uncover the truth behind this baffling claim. John recounted a lifetime of peculiar experiences that had left him feeling like a living enigma. It all began in his childhood when he noticed that his skin would emit a soft, bluish glow when the lights were turned off. His parents, initially dismissing it as an overactive imagination, soon realized that something extraordinary was indeed happening. The phenomenon was not limited to his skin; even his hair, eyes, and nails seemed to exude an ethereal radiance in the absence of light. As John grew older, he consulted various doctors and specialists, each one more mystified than the last. Countless tests, including skin biopsies, genetic analyses, and even luminescence studies, were conducted, but none provided any definitive answers. It was as if his condition defied the very principles of medical science. Despite the unusual nature of his condition, John had managed to lead a relatively normal life, shielding his secret from prying eyes. He had a small circle of close friends who accepted him for who he was, and he even managed to hold down a steady job in an office that allowed him to work primarily during daylight hours. But his condition was taking a toll on his mental and emotional well-being. The constant fear of being discovered, the isolation, and the unanswered questions had become overwhelming, prompting him to seek help once more.

Upon hearing John's story, I was both fascinated and skeptical. The scientific part of my mind questioned whether such a phenomenon could even exist. Yet, there was an undeniable sincerity in his voice, a vulnerability that spoke of the immense burden he had carried for so long. It was then that I made a commitment to unravel the mystery of John's condition, not only as a medical professional but as a fellow human being. The first step was to conduct a thorough physical examination. I observed John's skin closely, searching for any signs of a latent medical condition that might explain the glow. His skin, though pale, was unblemished and displayed no signs of inflammation or irritation. Even under a special light that could detect minor skin abnormalities, nothing unusual appeared. It was baffling. Next, we decided to perform every blood test available to us at that time in order to rule out any underlying hematological or biochemical abnormalities. John was cooperative throughout the process, even though he had been through numerous similar tests in the past. To our surprise, his blood work came back within the normal range for all parameters. There were no abnormalities that could explain the luminosity of his body. Time continued to pass and with the passing of each month I became more deeply engrossed in the quest to unravel this medical riddle. I consulted with colleagues, reached out to specialists in dermatology, genetics, and even physics, hoping to find someone who could shed light on John's condition. The more I delved into the case, the more I realized that this was a medical anomaly unlike any other. One theory that emerged from our discussions was that John might be emitting a form of biolumines-

cence, similar to certain deep-sea creatures. Bioluminescence is the ability of living organisms to produce light
through chemical reactions. While this phenomenon is
well-documented in marine life, its occurrence in
humans was virtually unheard of. To explore this possibility, we conducted extensive imaging studies and spec-
troscopy tests on John's skin to detect the presence of any
bioluminescent molecules. Unfortunately, our efforts
yielded no conclusive evidence.

The absence of a scientific explanation left us grappling with the possibility that John's condition might be
more metaphysical than physiological. Could it be that
he possessed some unique connection to the natural
world, harnessing a form of energy that defied our
current scientific understanding? While this hypothesis
sounded far-fetched, it was becoming increasingly challenging to dismiss. Throughout this journey, John
remained remarkably patient and resilient. He endured
countless tests, often with a smile that concealed his
inner turmoil. His determination to find answers kept
the rest of us not only inspired but humbled as well.
Personally, it drove me to continue the investigation with
unwavering commitment. One of the most pivotal
moments in our quest came when we consulted a
renowned physicist who specialized in quantum physics
and the study of biophotons. Biophotons are extremely

weak emissions of light that are produced by living organisms, including humans, as a result of various biochemical reactions. While these emissions are typically too faint to be visible to the naked eye, could John's condition somehow amplify them, making them visible as a soft glow? The physicist conducted a series of experiments, including sensitive biophoton imaging of John's body in complete darkness. To our astonishment, the results were remarkable. John's body did indeed emit biophotons at a much higher intensity than an average person. While this discovery was groundbreaking, it still didn't fully explain the vivid glow that John emitted. As we delved further into the quantum aspects of biophotons, the physicist introduced the concept of entanglement – a phenomenon where particles become interconnected in such a way that the state of one particle is instantly affected by the state of another, regardless of the distance between them. Could it be possible that John's biophotons were somehow entangled with those of the people around him, causing his glow to intensify in the dark? This theory, while intriguing, presented a host of questions that we couldn't easily answer. What caused this entanglement, and why was it unique to John? Was it purely a physical phenomenon, or did it have a deeper, metaphysical component? The answers remained elusive.

As our research continued, we expanded our investigations beyond the scientific realm. We consulted with
experts in metaphysics, spirituality, and even parapsy-
chology to explore the possibility that John's condition
had roots in the mystical or spiritual aspects of human
existence. While these discussions were speculative,
they opened our minds to the idea that the human body
and its connection to the universe might be more
complex and enigmatic than we could ever imagine.
Throughout this journey, I couldn't help but reflect on
the profound impact that John's condition had on me as
a medical professional. It was a humbling reminder that
our understanding of the human body, despite all the
advancements in science and medicine, was still incom-
plete. John's case challenged the very boundaries of our
knowledge and compelled us to question the mysteries
that lay hidden within us. Years passed and our investigations into John's condition continued, with no
definitive answers in sight. It became increasingly clear
that his condition was unlike anything ever documented
in medical literature. While we had made some progress
in understanding the biophotonic aspect of his glow, the
underlying mechanisms and the broader implications
remained shrouded in uncertainty. Despite the lack of
concrete answers for those first few years, John's journey
was not in vain. His courage in the face of adversity, his

unwavering determination to seek the truth, and his willingness to become a part of a scientific exploration into the unknown left an indelible mark on all those who were involved in his care. In many ways, he had become a symbol of human curiosity, resilience, and the unyielding pursuit of knowledge.

As our quest continued, we embarked on a series of experiments aimed at understanding the source and nature of John's unique bioluminescence. We enlisted the expertise of a team of biophysicists, who specialized in the study of light-emitting molecules and their interaction with biological systems. One of the key breakthroughs in our investigation came when we conducted a detailed analysis of John's skin samples under a powerful electron microscope. We discovered that his skin cells contained an unusually high number of specialized organelles called "photocytes." Phagocytes are cells found in certain bioluminescent organisms, such as fireflies and deep-sea creatures, that produce light through chemical reactions. In John's case, these photocytes were not only present but appeared to be hyperactive compared to those of a typical human. The photocytes contained a unique enzyme that catalyzed the production of photons, the smallest units of light. This enzyme, which we named "luminase," was responsible for the production of the bioluminescent glow that emanated from John's body. The discovery of luminase in John's skin cells was a groundbreaking revelation. It provided a scientific basis for the bioluminescence phenomenon that had baffled us for so long. But it also raised new questions: What had triggered the activation of luminase in John's cells, and why did his body produce bioluminescence at such an intensity? To explore these questions, we conducted a whole new series of genetic analyses on John's DNA. We discovered a unique genetic mutation that was present in his photocytes. This mutation, which we named "luminogene," was responsible for the overproduction of luminase and the subsequent bioluminescence. While the discovery of the luminogene mutation was a significant breakthrough, it didn't fully explain the source of the mutation itself. Genetic mutations typically occur as a result of various factors, including environmental exposures, radiation, or chemical influences. However, none of these factors seemed to apply to John's case. His environment and lifestyle were not significantly different from those of the general population, and he had not been exposed to any known mutagenic agents. As we delved deeper into the genetic aspects of John's condition, we discovered another remarkable phenomenon. The luminogene mutation was not present in any of John's immediate family members. This finding suggested that the mutation had occurred spontaneously in John's DNA, a rare and puzzling occurrence in genetics. The spontaneous nature of the mutation led us to consider the possibility that John's condition might be a one-of-a-kind genetic anomaly, an unprecedented occurrence in the history of medical science. The idea that his bioluminescence was the result of a completely unique genetic event was nothing short of awe-inspiring.

As our understanding of John's condition continued to evolve, we began to explore the broader implications of his unique genetic makeup. Could the discovery of the luminogene mutation hold the key to unlocking new advancements in biophotonics, the study of biologically produced light? Could it have applications in fields such as medicine, bioimaging, or even energy production? To answer these questions, we collaborated with researchers from various scientific disciplines, including biophotonics, genetics, and materials science. Together, we embarked on a multidisciplinary research project aimed at harnessing the potential of John's luminogene mutation for practical applications. While these research endeavors were in their early stages and faced significant challenges, they represented a testament to the profound impact that John's condition had on the scientific community. His unique genetic anomaly had opened doors to new realms of discovery, pushing the boundaries of what was previously thought possible. Throughout this scientific journey, John remained an active and enthusiastic participant. He was not only eager to contribute to our research efforts but also hopeful that his condition could ultimately lead to advancements that would benefit others. His unwavering optimism and resilience in the face of adversity continued to inspire everyone involved in his care. Our team of physicists and biologists began to investigate whether the luminase enzyme in John's cells exhibited quantum properties that played a role in the production of bioluminescence. Quantum entanglement, the phenomenon where particles become interconnected regardless of distance, emerged as a particularly intriguing concept. Could it be possible that the photocytes in John's skin cells were somehow entangled with one another, facilitating the synchronized production of bioluminescence? The idea that quantum entanglement might be involved in John's condition raised profound questions about the nature of life, light, and the interconnectedness of the universe. To explore this hypothesis, we conducted a series of experiments that involved measuring the quantum states of the photons emitted by John's skin cells. The results were astonishing. We observed a remarkable degree of quantum entanglement among the photons, suggesting that they were indeed interconnected in a way that defied classical physics.

The discovery of quantum entanglement in John's bioluminescent cells was a paradigm-shifting moment in our research. It not only provided a plausible explanation for the synchronized glow of his body but also opened up new avenues of exploration in quantum biology. The implications of this finding extended far beyond the realm of medical science, reaching into the fundamental nature of reality itself. As our understanding of John's condition deepened, we found ourselves at the crossroads of science and philosophy. The mysteries surrounding his bioluminescence forced us to confront profound questions about the nature of consciousness, the interconnectedness of all life, and the boundaries of human knowledge. In the years that followed, our research into John's condition continued to advance, yielding new insights and discoveries that pushed the boundaries of scientific knowledge. The potential applications of his unique genetic anomaly continued to expand, offering hope for advancements in fields as diverse as medicine, bioimaging, and quantum biology. Throughout it all, John remained at the center of our efforts, a beacon of resilience and hope in the face of the extraordinary. His story had transcended the realm of medical anomaly and become a testament to the boundless potential of human curiosity and the enduring quest for knowledge. As I reflect on my remarkable journey with John and the profound impact he has had on the world of science and medicine, I am reminded of the words of Albert Einstein: "The most beautiful thing we can experience is the mysterious. It is the source of all true art and science." John's condition was, and continues to be, a source of wonder and inspiration, a reminder that the mysteries of the universe are waiting to be uncovered by those who dare to explore the unknown. John's story and his mysterious medical anomaly reinforced for me that the human desire to understand and explore the mysteries of the universe knows no bounds. John's journey has left an indelible mark on the world of science and medicine, challenging us to think beyond the boundaries of what we know and to embrace the profound mysteries that surround us and I am honored to have been a part of it and to have been able to share his story with you today.

CHAPTER EIGHT

A COMPLEX PUZZLE

I'LL NEVER FORGET the day when everything changed for me. Professionally I thought that I had seen it all and even though I knew I still had a lot to learn, I never thought a case would come across my desk that would leave me so stumped I would eventually start to question whether or not I even belonged in the field of medicine in the first place. Being a doctor was the pride of my life back then and it still is today. At the time I thought about quitting but what they don't and can't teach you in medical school is that the cases that make you question everything you thought you knew are the ones that not only change you as a person for the better, but they also make you much better at what you do and enable you to eventually save more lived. The day is etched into my memory like a complex medical puzzle.

It was a day when the boundaries of my knowledge and experience were pushed to their limits. It all began when an enigmatic patient walked through the doors of our clinic, his very existence shrouded in a cloak of medical mystery. As a seasoned medical professional, I had encountered a multitude of cases throughout my career, but none quite like this. The patient, whom I'll refer to as Mr. A, was a man in his early forties. His initial symptoms were perplexing: extreme fatigue, persistent joint pain, and a disconcerting yellowing of the skin and eyes. He described these symptoms as having plagued him for the past several months, and they were progressively worsening. Upon Mr. A's arrival, my team and I wasted no time. We conducted a thorough physical examination, reviewing his medical history, medications, and lifestyle. Despite our best efforts, nothing in his background seemed to account for this peculiar constellation of symptoms. Laboratory tests were ordered, and we anxiously awaited the results.

The initial lab findings threw us into further bewilderment. His liver enzymes were alarmingly elevated, and his bilirubin levels were off the charts. Yet, his liver function tests suggested his liver was surprisingly resilient, despite this apparent insult. Our minds were filled with questions, hypotheses, and an increasing sense of urgency. We scheduled a liver biopsy, hoping it would provide some clarity. However, the results only deepened the mystery. The biopsy showed mild inflammation and minimal fibrosis, but nothing that could explain the severe jaundice and debilitating fatigue that had overtaken Mr. A's life. Our team huddled together, reviewing the results again and again, searching for any overlooked clues. Days turned into weeks, and we embarked on a comprehensive battery of tests and consultations with specialists from various fields. We considered autoimmune diseases, infectious agents, genetic disorders, and even rare malignancies. The puzzle pieces just didn't fit. As our patient's health continued to decline, the sense of urgency weighed heavily on our shoulders. Then, one fateful afternoon, a light appeared at the end of the tunnel. Our head of gastroenterology, Dr. Patel, stumbled upon an obscure case report buried in the annals of medical literature. It described a condition known as "Crigler-Najjar syndrome." This extremely rare genetic disorder resulted in hyperbilirubinemia, similar to what Mr. A was experiencing. But Crigler-Najjar syndrome was typically a congenital condition, present from birth. Could it really be the answer? Our hopes were dashed when Mr. A's genetic testing returned negative for Crigler-Najjar syndrome. It was yet another dead-end, but we refused to give up. The determination of our team only grew stronger as we delved deeper into the abyss of this medical enigma.

One night, as I sat poring over Mr. A's file, a small detail caught my eye. It was a comment from his wife, who had mentioned an episode of food poisoning they had both experienced while vacationing in a remote part of South America. It was a seemingly insignificant piece of information, but it ignited a spark of curiosity within me. Could it be that this mysterious illness had originated from that trip? I began researching infectious diseases prevalent in the region they had visited. One name stood out—Leptospirosis. It was a bacterial infection known to cause liver damage, among other symptoms. Could this be the elusive diagnosis we had been searching for? We immediately ran a battery of tests for Leptospirosis, and the results came back positive. Finally, we had a diagnosis. But the road ahead was still treacherous. Leptospirosis can cause severe liver damage, and Mr. A's case had gone untreated for months, leading to a potentially life-threatening situation. We started him on a course of antibiotics, hoping to halt the progression of the disease. However, given the extent of the damage, a liver transplant became a looming possibility. The thought of such a major surgery was daunting, but it was our patient's best chance at a normal life. Months passed, and Mr. A's condition slowly improved. His jaundice began to recede, and his energy levels increased. With each follow-up appointment, our optimism grew. We grew close during this journey, and our conversations extended beyond medical updates. We learned about his hobbies, his love for literature, and the dreams he held dear. It was these personal connections that made our work all the more rewarding. One afternoon, as I sat across from Mr. A during one of our follow-up appointments, he shared his gratitude for the unwavering support he had received from our medical team. His voice trembled with emotion as he spoke about the fear and uncertainty that had clouded his life before his diagnosis. He expressed profound gratitude for the dedication of the healthcare professionals who had refused to give up on him. Our team was deeply moved by his words. It was a poignant reminder of why we had chosen this profession—to make a difference in the lives of individuals like Mr. A, to offer hope when it seemed elusive, and to pursue answers to medical mysteries no matter how inscrutable they may be.

Throughout Mr. A's recovery, we continued to explore the underlying factors that had made his case so unique. Leptospirosis, the bacterial infection that had initially eluded diagnosis, was known for causing a range of symptoms, but severe liver damage on this scale was a rarity. We collaborated with infectious disease specialists to gain a deeper understanding of the intricacies of the disease. Research in the field of infectious diseases had revealed that certain strains of Leptospira bacteria could cause more severe liver involvement than others. Mr. A's case appeared to involve one of these particularly virulent strains. The exact mechanism by which the bacteria had wreaked havoc on his liver was still not entirely clear, but it was a piece of the puzzle that was slowly falling into place. While Mr. A continued to heal, we were also mindful of the potential long-term effects of his illness. Chronic liver disease could lead to complications such as cirrhosis and portal hypertension. To monitor his progress and mitigate these risks, we scheduled regular liver function tests and imaging studies. During this period of continued observation, we discovered another facet of Mr. A's medical journey. He was grappling with anxiety and depression, common emotional responses to a severe and life-altering illness. We recognized the importance of addressing not only his physical health but also his emotional well-being. Our team collaborated with mental health professionals to provide Mr. A with the support he needed. Therapy sessions, both individual and group, became an integral part of his recovery plan. It was heartening to witness his gradual transformation—not just physically but mentally as well. As Mr. A's health improved, he was able to return to many of the activities he had once enjoyed. He rekindled his passion for literature, joining a local book club, and even began volunteering at a community library. His resilience was nothing short of inspiring, and his story served as a source of motivation for our entire team.

With each passing day, Mr. A's liver function tests continued to improve. The once-elevated liver enzymes gradually returned to normal levels, a testament to the remarkable regenerative capacity of the liver. It was an awe-inspiring demonstration of the body's ability to heal when given the right care and support. Despite the progress, the shadow of a potential liver transplant still loomed. We knew that the damage to Mr. A's liver had been extensive, and while it was healing, there were no guarantees that it would fully recover. The decision to pursue a transplant remained a topic of discussion, with both its risks and benefits carefully weighed. Ultimately, it was a multidisciplinary team of medical experts that made the decision. After a series of extensive evaluations, Mr. A was deemed a suitable candidate for a liver transplant. The news was met with mixed emotions— hope for a future free from the constraints of his illness, but also apprehension about the surgery itself. The call finally came one brisk autumn morning. A liver had become available—a precious gift from a generous donor and their family. The transplant surgery was scheduled, and our team prepared meticulously. It was a day filled with tension, hope, and the anticipation of a new beginning. The surgery itself was a success. Mr. A received a healthy liver that promised a new lease on life. It was a testament to the incredible advancements in medical science and the selflessness of organ donors. In the days that followed, Mr. A's recovery was closely monitored in the intensive care unit. The post-transplant period was marked by a combination of hope and vigilance. While the surgery had been successful, there was always a risk of complications or rejection. Mr. A's immune system would need to adapt to its new host and accept the foreign organ as its own.

Immunosuppressive medications were carefully administered to prevent rejection while minimizing the risk of infection. The weeks following the transplant were filled with frequent visits to the clinic, extensive lab work, and adjustments to his medication regimen. Throughout this journey, Mr. A's family remained a steadfast source of support. His wife, children, and close friends were by his side every step of the way. The emotional toll of a serious illness and transplant surgery could not be underestimated, and the importance of a strong support system could not be overstated. As the months passed, Mr. A's strength grew, and his gratitude deepened. He often spoke of the incredible journey he had undertaken, from the bewildering onset of symptoms to the life-saving transplant surgery. He had emerged on the other side with a renewed appreciation for life and a profound sense of purpose. Mr. A's story became a symbol of hope within our clinic—a reminder that even the most mysterious and challenging medical cases could be solved with determination, collaboration, and unwavering commitment to the well-being of the patient. It underscored the importance of pushing the boundaries of medical knowledge and never giving up in the face of uncertainty.

Today, Mr. A continues to thrive. His life has been transformed, not only by the miracle of modern medicine but also by his indomitable spirit and the unwavering support of his loved ones. He has become an advocate for organ donation, sharing his story to raise awareness about the life-saving impact of organ transplantation. As for our medical team, Mr. A's case left an indelible mark on each of us. It reinforced our dedication to the pursuit of answers, the advancement of medical science, and the unwavering support of our patients. It was a reminder that every individual who walks through our clinic doors brings with them a unique journey, and it is our privilege and responsibility to be a part of that journey. The story of Mr. A's medical odyssey is a testament to the power of perseverance, collaboration, and the relentless pursuit of answers in the face of medical mysteries. It highlights the profound impact of organ transplantation and the importance of emotional support in the healing process. Mr. A's journey serves as a source of inspiration for both patients and healthcare professionals, a reminder that hope and healing are attainable, even in the most challenging of circumstances.

CHAPTER NINE

HE FELT IN COLOR

THROUGHOUT MY EXTENSIVE career as a medical professional, which spans over three decades, I have encountered numerous fascinating cases. However, one particular medical anomaly stands out in my memory— an extraordinary occurrence that defied conventional medical understanding. For some reason I've been thinking about this particular case a lot lately. Maybe it's because I am so close to finally retiring and wish sometimes I had been challenged more throughout my career like I was in this particular case. It's certainly the most interesting case I've ever been involved with, but also it was the most frustrating and made me question everything I thought I knew and was like starting all over again as far as my medical knowledge and expertise were concerned. I decided to share the details of this unique case, finally, going over what happened and the subsequent impact it had on my career. In the interest of privacy, I will call the exceptional individual at the heart of this story Alex.

Alex's story began on an ordinary day in the clinic. An unassuming figure, Alex walked into my examination room, carrying a secret that would leave me astounded and deeply engrossed in a medical mystery like no other. Alex was in his twenties, with a warm smile that masked the enigma he brought into the room. Their chief complaint was anything but ordinary. Alex claimed to possess an extraordinary sense—one that enabled him to perceive colors through touch. Not just any colors, but specific shades and hues that corresponded to different textures and materials. To put it simply, he claimed that he could 'see' the world not with his eyes, but through his fingertips. As a medical professional and an adamant skeptic, I approached the case with a mixture of intrigue and caution. Such a phenomenon was far from common in the realm of medical science, but little did I know then that we were about to embark on a journey that would challenge my understanding of the human senses. Our first step was a comprehensive physical examination. I needed to rule out any potential physical or neurological causes for Alex's extraordinary ability. Surprisingly, the examination revealed nothing out of the ordinary. His sensory receptors, nerve pathways, and brain functions appeared to be in perfect working order. Next, we initiated a battery of tests to evaluate the extent and accuracy of Alex's sensory perception. We presented him with various textured materials, fabrics, and objects while blindfolded. It was astonishing to witness Alex's ability to consistently and accurately describe the colors associated with each texture. Alex's condition, which we eventually began to refer to as "sensory chromesthesia," was truly unique. Sensory chromesthesia allowed him to perceive colors through touch in a way that defied conventional understanding. When he touched different textures or materials, he would vividly experience the sensation as a specific color. It was as if his fingertips were connected to a palette of colors, each texture invoking a distinct shade or hue. What further confounded us was that Alex's descriptions were not vague or generalized. He didn't simply say, "This feels soft," or "This feels rough." Instead, he would say things like, "This fabric feels like a deep royal blue," or "This surface is reminiscent of a bright, sunlit yellow." It was as if his fingers were connected to a vibrant palette of colors, each texture a distinct shade waiting to be revealed.

The next logical step was to explore the neurological

pathways responsible for this exceptional sensory perception. We referred Alex to a team of neurologists who conducted a battery of brain imaging scans and sensory processing assessments. The results, however, were baffling. There were no discernible abnormalities in his brain structure or sensory processing centers. As we delved deeper into Alex's medical history, certain patterns began to emerge. His unique sensory perception had been present since childhood and had never caused any distress or discomfort. In fact, Alex had adapted to his extraordinary ability with remarkable ease. He described how, as a child, he had used this 'color-touch' sense to navigate the world and even to distinguish objects in complete darkness. With no apparent physical or neurological explanation, we started to consider alternative possibilities. Could this be a manifestation of a rare and as-yet-undocumented sensory phenomenon? We decided to cast a wider net and reached out to experts in the field of sensory perception and synesthesia—the phenomenon where sensory experiences become intertwined. While Alex's case was unique, it bore some resemblance to the sensory blending seen in certain forms of synesthesia.

A renowned synesthesia researcher joined our team, and together, we embarked on a series of rigorous assessments to explore the potential synesthetic nature of

Alex's condition. We conducted a battery of tests to determine whether his sensory perceptions triggered other sensory experiences, such as taste or sound. As time passed, the challenges posed by Alex's unexplained sensory chromesthesia became increasingly evident. One of the most striking aspects was the impact on his daily life. While his ability was undeniably extraordinary, it also introduced unique challenges and uncertainties. Simple tasks that we take for granted, such as choosing clothing based on texture or cooking by touch, were far more complex for him. Alex often described the experience of navigating the world as akin to living in a constant state of sensory richness. While this might sound fascinating, it also came with moments of overwhelming sensory input. Imagine touching a seemingly ordinary object and suddenly being inundated with a burst of vibrant colors. For Alex, this was a regular occurrence, and it required an extraordinary level of adaptability. Surprisingly, our findings indicated that Alex's 'color-touch' sense remained remarkably distinct and did not induce synesthetic experiences. As we delved deeper into our research, we began to consider the broader implications of Alex's unique sensory perception. Could this phenomenon offer insights into our understanding of human perception and the brain's extraordinary adaptability? We explored the possibility that this ability might be rooted in a heightened sensitivity to minute differences in texture and temperature—a sensory superpower that the rest of us simply lacked. The more we delved into Alex's case, the more it became apparent that his condition was not a disorder but rather a remarkable gift—an extraordinary sensory perception that provided him with a unique lens through which to experience the world. To provide Alex with some closure and understanding of his unique condition, we continued our research, collaborating with experts from various fields. We embarked on a journey to map the neural pathways associated with his 'color-touch' sense, hoping to unravel the biological basis of this remarkable ability. As the years passed, Alex's story continued to captivate our attention and fuel our curiosity. We remained in close contact, sharing our findings and exploring the potential applications of their sensory perception in fields such as art, design, and education. Alex's extraordinary gift was not just a medical anomaly; it was a testament to the boundless wonders of the human brain and the limitless potential for discovery within the realm of medicine. But what were we dealing with? Well, that's still a question I struggle with to this day. Through the years one of the most profound challenges, we faced in Alex's case was the lack of a conclusive explanation for his extraordinary sensory perception. While we had ruled out physical and neurological causes, the absence of a clear scientific understanding left us with a sense of incompleteness—a nagging question that lingered in the background of our research.

First and foremost, the absence of a definitive diagnosis meant that we couldn't provide Alex with a concrete explanation for his unique ability. This lack of closure was emotionally challenging for him, as it left him with a sense of being an outlier, an anomaly in a world that often values conformity. He grappled with questions about his place in society and whether his condition would ever be fully understood or accepted. It also meant that Alex faced skepticism and misunderstanding from those around him. People found it difficult to comprehend the reality of his sensory perceptions, often attributing it to exaggeration or imagination. This lack of understanding led to feelings of isolation and a sense of being 'othered'—challenges that weighed heavily on Alex's emotional well-being. For our medical team, the inability to pinpoint the exact cause of Alex's 'color-touch' sense was equally frustrating. It was a reminder that, despite the advances in medical science, there were still aspects of the human body and brain that remained shrouded in mystery. We had encountered a phenomenon that defied our current understanding, and it was a humbling experience for us as healthcare professionals. The lack of a clear diagnosis also had implications for potential treatment or intervention. Without knowing the underlying cause of Alex's sensory perception, we couldn't explore targeted therapies or interventions that might have alleviated any associated challenges or discomfort. This left us with limited options for supporting Alex in managing his unique gift. Moreover, we grappled with the ethical and philosophical implications of Alex's case. It raised questions about the nature of human perception and the boundaries of what we consider 'normal.' Were there other individuals with similar extraordinary abilities who had simply gone unnoticed or unreported? Alex's case challenged our preconceptions about sensory perception and the potential for hidden talents within the human population. Another challenge we faced was the limited precedent in the medical literature. Alex's condition appeared to be one-of-a-kind, and we struggled to find similar cases that could provide insights or comparative data. This lack of a reference point made it difficult to contextualize and understand the significance of their unique sensory perception.

Despite these challenges, our commitment to Alex and his journey remained unwavering. We continued to explore potential avenues for research and collaboration, reaching out to experts from various disciplines, including psychology, neuroscience, and sensory perception. We hoped that by casting a wider net and sharing Alex's story with the broader scientific community, we might eventually uncover clues that could shed light on their condition. In the end, the absence of definitive answers in Alex's case was a testament to the complexities of the human body and the limitations of our current scientific knowledge. It reminded us that medicine is an evolving field, and there are still frontiers of discovery waiting to be explored. Alex's case underscored the importance of curiosity, perseverance, and interdisciplinary collaboration in the pursuit of medical understanding. As I reflect on my journey with Alex, I am reminded that not all medical mysteries are meant to be solved in a neat and tidy fashion. Some cases challenge us to think beyond conventional boundaries and to embrace the unknown with humility and curiosity. Alex's unique sensory perception, while still a puzzle, remains a source of inspiration—a reminder that the human body is capable of remarkable surprises that defy our understanding. In the end, it is not always about finding answers, but about the journey of exploration itself. It is about the questions that drive us forward, the mysteries that ignite our curiosity, and the individuals like Alex who remind us that the human experience is a tapestry woven with threads of diversity and wonder. As we continue our pursuit of medical knowledge, we carry with us the memory of Alex's extraordinary journey—a journey that challenges us to remain open to the mysteries that await our discovery and to embrace the limitless potential of the human body and mind. I'll never forget Alex and we speak on the phone several times a year, even after all these years have passed. He's like an old friend and I've gotten to know the family and somewhat, if maybe a bit on the periphery, I've become like a part of his extended family. Working so closely with him for all those years, even after he thought we had long since decided there was no hope in ever finding answers for him, let alone in finding a cure for whatever this thing was that was affecting him so greatly, he's become a very important person in my life, both person-ally and professionally and I hope in writing this story he will read it and understand just how much I really mean that, and how much he means to all of us who are still with him, even if only in our minds, throughout the extraordinary journey of his life.

CHAPTER TEN

A BLUSH DISCOLORIZATION

I'VE SPENT my career as a medical professional treating a wide array of patients and navigating the complexities of the human body. I've seen my fair share of medical mysteries, but one case, in particular, stands out as the most perplexing and rare condition I've ever encountered. It was a puzzle that tested the limits of medical knowledge and our ability to find answers. The patient in question, let's call him Mr. W, was a middle-aged man who had led a fairly ordinary life until he started experiencing a series of baffling symptoms. He first sought medical attention when he noticed that his skin had taken on an unusual bluish-gray tint, a condition known as cyanosis. This change in skin color was especially prominent in his lips and fingertips. At first, Mr. W dismissed it as a temporary issue, perhaps a reaction to the cold weather or a sign of poor circulation. But as the days passed, his symptoms worsened. He began to feel an overwhelming fatigue, as if his body was constantly working overtime just to keep him going. His appetite waned, and he lost a significant amount of weight in a short period. Concerned, Mr. W scheduled an appointment with his primary care physician. His doctor, equally puzzled by the unusual presentation, ran a battery of tests, including blood work and imaging scans. The results were baffling—there were no apparent abnormalities in his blood chemistry, and his organs appeared to be functioning normally. Yet, the cyanosis persisted, and Mr. W's condition continued to deteriorate.

Recognizing the need for a specialist, Mr. W was referred to our medical center, where I became involved in his care. As a team, we reviewed his medical history, conducted a thorough physical examination, and ordered additional tests to get to the bottom of his mysterious ailment. One of the most striking aspects of Mr. W's condition was the bluish discoloration of his skin. Cyanosis typically indicates a lack of oxygen in the blood, which can be caused by various underlying issues, including respiratory and cardiovascular problems. However, our initial tests ruled out these common causes. Further investigations revealed that Mr. W's oxygen levels were within the normal range, and his lung and heart function were adequate. This ruled out conditions like pulmonary embolism, heart failure, or chronic obstructive pulmonary disease (COPD). It was as if the oxygen in his blood was mysteriously failing to reach his tissues, causing his skin to take on that disconcerting hue. As we delved deeper into Mr. W's case, we began to notice another troubling symptom—a persistent cough that produced a frothy, pink-tinged sputum. This symptom, along with the cyanosis, raised concerns about a potential lung-related issue. We decided to perform a bronchoscopy, a procedure that would allow us to visualize the inside of Mr. W's airways.

During the bronchoscopy, we discovered an unusual finding. Small, translucent nodules dotted the inner lining of his bronchial tubes, and they appeared to be causing some degree of obstruction. Biopsies of these nodules were taken for further analysis, and we anxiously awaited the results. Meanwhile, Mr. W's condition continued to worsen. He struggled to breathe and often required supplemental oxygen to maintain his oxygen saturation levels. His fatigue was so profound that he could barely get out of bed, and his weight loss was alarming. We had to act swiftly to uncover the root cause of his ailment and formulate an appropriate treatment plan. The biopsy results arrived, and they were nothing short of astonishing. The translucent nodules in Mr. W's bronchial tubes were composed of an unusual substance called amyloid. Amyloid is an abnormal protein that can accumulate in various tissues and organs, disrupting their normal function. In Mr. W's case, the amyloid deposits were blocking his airways, preventing proper airflow and oxygen exchange. Amyloidosis, a condition characterized by the abnormal buildup of amyloid protein, was a rare and concerning diagnosis. It can affect multiple organ systems, leading to a wide range of symptoms. However, Mr. W's case was even more unusual because amyloidosis typically presents with a reddish-brown discoloration of the skin, not the distinctive bluish-gray hue that he exhibited.

To determine the extent of the amyloidosis and its impact on Mr. W's body, we conducted a series of specialized tests, including serum and urine protein electrophoresis, bone marrow biopsy, and cardiac imaging. These tests revealed that his amyloidosis primarily affected his respiratory system, with minimal involvement in other organs. The next step was to identify the specific type of amyloid protein responsible for Mr. W's condition. Amyloidosis can be categorized into several subtypes based on the specific protein involved. The most common form is AL amyloidosis, which results from the buildup of abnormal immunoglobulin light chains. However, Mr. W's tests showed no evidence of AL amyloidosis. Instead, he was diagnosed with a rare variant known as AA amyloidosis. AA amyloidosis is associated with chronic inflammation or infection and is characterized by the accumulation of a protein called serum amyloid A (SAA). In Mr. W's case, we suspected that a chronic, low-grade inflammatory process was triggering the production of SAA, leading to the formation of amyloid deposits in his bronchial tubes. Treatment for amyloidosis typically involves addressing the underlying cause of the protein buildup and managing the associated symptoms. In Mr. W's case, we focused on reducing the inflammation driving his condition. He was started on anti-inflammatory medications, and his response was closely monitored. Over the course of several months, Mr. W's condition gradually improved. The bluish-gray tint to his skin began to fade, and he regained some of his lost weight. His cough diminished, and his oxygen requirements decreased. It was a slow and challenging journey, but we were finally making progress.

To prevent further complications and recurrence of AA amyloidosis, we continued to manage Mr. W's underlying inflammatory condition diligently. Regular follow-up appointments, blood tests, and imaging studies allowed us to track his progress and adjust his treatment plan as needed. As time passed, Mr. W's health continued to improve. The once-mysterious bluish hue of his skin was replaced by a healthier, natural color. He regained his energy and was able to resume many of the activities he had enjoyed before the onset of his illness. Reflecting on Mr. W's case, I couldn't help but marvel at the complexity of the human body and the challenges that rare medical conditions present. It was a stark reminder that medicine is an ever-evolving field, and there is always more to learn and discover. Mr. W's journey highlighted the importance of persistence and collaboration in the medical community. It took a team of dedicated healthcare professionals, each contributing their expertise, to unravel the mystery of his condition and develop an effective treatment plan. In the end, Mr. W's story really says a lot about the human spirit, a human being's ability to bounce back even after the very worst and most dire of circumstances and the power of medical science. His rare and enigmatic condition tested our knowledge and capabilities, but with determination and a multidisciplinary approach, we were able to provide him with the care he needed.

While AA amyloidosis remains a rare and challenging condition, Mr. W's successful treatment offers hope to others facing similar diagnoses. It underscores the importance of early detection, accurate diagnosis, and tailored treatment plans in managing rare and complex medical conditions. As a medical professional, I continue to be inspired by cases like Mr. W's, which remind me of the boundless possibilities within the field of medicine. Each patient presents a unique puzzle, and it is our duty to seek answers, provide care, and ultimately improve their quality of life. Mr. W's journey may have been marked by uncertainty and adversity, but it also exemplifies the remarkable resilience of the human body and the unwavering dedication of those in the medical profession. His story serves as a reminder that, in the face of rare and mysterious medical conditions, hope, persistence, and collaboration can lead to answers, solutions, and ultimately, healing. As Mr. W's condition continued to improve, he became an integral part of our ongoing research efforts. His unique case presented an opportunity to deepen our understanding of AA amyloidosis and the mechanisms behind its development. We collaborated with researchers from various disciplines, pooling our knowledge and resources to investigate this rare variant of the disease.

One of the key questions we sought to answer was the origin of the chronic inflammation that had triggered Mr. W's AA amyloidosis. While it was clear that inflammation played a central role in his condition, identifying the underlying cause proved to be a complex puzzle. Extensive testing revealed that Mr. W. had a history of recurrent respiratory infections, which had often gone unnoticed due to their mild and intermittent nature. We suspected that these low-grade infections had been the source of the chronic inflammation driving his AA amyloidosis. To address this, Mr. W was referred to a specialist in infectious diseases who conducted a thorough evaluation. Additional testing, including blood cultures and imaging studies, confirmed the presence of a chronic, low-grade respiratory infection that had gone untreated for an extended period. Treatment for the infection was initiated promptly, with a targeted course of antibiotics. It was a challenging process, as the infection had become deeply entrenched, but we were determined to eliminate the source of inflammation and prevent further amyloid deposits. Over time, Mr. W's condition improved dramatically. The chronic inflammation began to subside, and the levels of serum amyloid A (SAA) in his blood, a key marker of AA amyloidosis, gradually decreased. Repeat bronchoscopies showed a significant reduction in the amyloid deposits within his bronchial tubes. With continued treatment and monitoring, Mr. W's respiratory function improved significantly. His oxygen requirements diminished further, and his cough resolved entirely. It was a testament to the power of targeted therapy and a multidisciplinary approach in managing complex medical conditions.

As we celebrated Mr. W's remarkable progress, we also recognized the invaluable contribution his case had made to the field of medicine. Our research efforts, driven by his unique presentation, had yielded insights into the mechanisms of AA amyloidosis and the importance of early detection and intervention. Mr. W's journey was not without its challenges, and he had faced moments of uncertainty and despair. However, his resilience and determination had carried him through, and he had emerged on the other side with renewed health and hope. Looking back on Mr. W's case, I couldn't help but reflect on the broader lessons it had taught us as medical professionals. It underscored the importance of thorough and persistent investigation, especially in cases of rare and elusive conditions. It demonstrated the power of collaboration across medical specialties, where diverse expertise could lead to breakthroughs in understanding and treatment. Perhaps most importantly, Mr. W's story emphasized the critical role of the patient in the journey toward healing. His willingness to participate in our research efforts, to endure the challenges of treatment, and to maintain a positive outlook had been instrumental in his recovery. In the end, Mr. W's case served as a beacon of hope for others facing rare and mysterious medical conditions. It showcased the potential for progress and breakthroughs, even in the most challenging and enigmatic cases. As medical professionals, we are continually humbled by the resilience of our patients and the complexities of the human body. Every case, like Mr. W's, presents an opportunity to learn, to innovate, and to advance the boundaries of medical knowledge. Mr. W's journey may have tested our knowledge and capabilities, but it also reaffirmed our commitment to the relentless pursuit of answers and solutions. It served as a reminder that, in the world of medicine, every patient's journey serves as a reminder and each patient is living proof of the remarkable resilience of the human spirit and the limitless potential for discovery and healing. I am grateful to have been a part of Mr. W's journey and to have witnessed the remarkable progress he made. His story reminds us that, even in the face of the most baffling medical mysteries, there is always the potential for discovery and healing. It reinforces our commitment to the pursuit of answers and solutions, no matter how rare or elusive the condition may be. As for Mr. W, he has resumed a fulfilling life, free from the constraints of AA amyloidosis. His skin has regained its natural color, and his energy has returned. He continues to inspire us with his resilience and optimism, a living testament to the power of perseverance and the possibilities within the field of medicine. In the end, while Mr. W's case challenged our knowledge and capabilities, it also reaffirmed our commitment to the relentless pursuit of answers and solutions. It served as a reminder that, in the world of medicine, every patient's journey is a testament to the remarkable resilience of the human spirit and the limitless potential for discovery and healing.

CHAPTER ELEVEN

ALOHA

I HAD BEEN EAGERLY AWAITING this moment for years – a vacation to Hawaii, a well-deserved break from my demanding role as an ER doctor. Five years of relentless work had taken its toll, and this trip was my chance to finally unwind and recharge. The excitement surged through me as I made my way through the airport terminal, my suitcase trailing behind.

After passing through security with the efficiency of someone who knew the process well, I headed towards the gate where my flight to paradise awaited. However, I couldn't resist the temptation to start my vacation a bit early. I stopped at a nearby bar, ordered a drink, and savored the taste of freedom. The atmosphere was filled with the anticipation of travelers embarking on their

adventures, and I couldn't help but join in the pre-vaca-
tion revelry.

Feeling the need to prepare for the long flight ahead,
I made a quick stop at a convenience store within the
terminal. I picked up some gum to help with the dreaded
pressure changes during takeoff and landing and
grabbed a bottle of water to stay hydrated. With these
essentials in hand, I finally made my way to the gate,
ready to board the plane that would transport me to the
idyllic Hawaiian Islands.

As I boarded the plane, I couldn't help but notice the
mix of passengers on board. It seemed that the flight was
filled with a diverse group of individuals, each with their
own story. Honeymooning couples reveled in their
newlywed bliss, while excited spring breakers looked
forward to unforgettable adventures. There were also a
few families on board, complete with small children
whose eager chatter added a touch of youthful energy to
the atmosphere.

The plane's engines roared to life, and with a gentle
pushback from the gate, we began our ascent into the
cerulean skies. The sensation of leaving the ground
behind and soaring into the air always held a special
kind of magic for me, even after all these years. I settled
into my seat, ready to enjoy the in-flight entertainment
and, more importantly, some well-deserved relaxation.

About two hours into the flight, as I was engrossed in a captivating movie, a flight attendant approached me. Her demeanor was a mix of concern and urgency, and she asked a question that instantly shifted the course of my vacation. "Are you a doctor?" she inquired, her words hanging in the air. It was a question I had been asked countless times during my career, and I had never imagined that my skills would be needed on a plane bound for paradise.

With a sense of responsibility that came naturally to me as a doctor, I replied affirmatively. The flight attendant explained that there was a medical emergency unfolding in the back of the plane, and they needed my assistance. I quickly gathered my belongings and followed her down the narrow aisle, my heart pounding with a mixture of apprehension and determination.

As I reached the back of the plane, I was met with a scene of organized chaos. A passenger, a young bride, had fallen unconscious, and concerned onlookers had gathered around her. The flight attendants were doing their best to attend to her, but it was clear that they needed medical expertise to assess the situation.

I introduced myself and immediately began to assess the unconscious woman. Her vital signs were stable, but her breathing was shallow, and she showed no signs of regaining consciousness. The flight attendants explained that she had complained of feeling unwell before collapsing, and they were unsure of the cause.

In the confined and pressurized cabin of an airplane, my role as an ER doctor was abruptly summoned into action, plunging me into a high-stakes medical scenario. In response to the flight attendant's urgent plea for assistance, I promptly gathered the limited medical equipment at our disposal and initiated a thorough examination of the patient at hand. It swiftly became apparent that the situation was more complex than initially anticipated, as the patient was not only facing a medical crisis but was also four months pregnant, adding an additional layer of complexity to the unfolding drama at 30,000 feet.

The gravity of the situation demanded my full attention. With the aid of the cabin crew, we managed to create a makeshift treatment area in the cramped confines of the airplane's rear section. My clinical assessment revealed concerning symptoms that included chest pain, shortness of breath, and a fluctuating heart rate. As I delved deeper into the patient's medical history, it became evident that her condition was exacerbated by the fact that she was in her second trimester of pregnancy.

The unique challenges presented by the patient's pregnancy required a careful and considered approach.

While maintaining her cardiovascular stability was paramount, we also had to ensure the well-being of both the patient and her unborn child. With limited resources and the assistance of the flight attendants, I administered oxygen to optimize her oxygen saturation and initiated measures to alleviate her discomfort. It was a race against time, and every decision weighed heavily, as the intricate interplay between maternal and fetal health hung in the balance amidst the backdrop of a high-altitude emergency.

With limited resources at my disposal, I had to make crucial decisions about how to proceed. I instructed the flight attendants to inform the flight deck of the medical emergency and to prepare for an emergency landing if necessary. Meanwhile, I initiated interventions to stabilize the patient's condition and administered oxygen to improve her oxygen saturation.

The challenge of providing medical care in midair added an extra layer of complexity to the situation. I had to rely on my clinical judgment and the support of the flight attendants to ensure the safety and well-being of the unconscious passenger. The cabin crew remained remarkably composed, assisting me with tasks as we worked together to manage the crisis.

As we continued to monitor the patient's condition, the flight attendants offered reassurance to the other passengers, who had grown understandably anxious. In the midst of this high-stress situation, I found myself drawing upon not only my medical expertise but also my ability to communicate effectively and provide a sense of calm in the face of uncertainty.

Time seemed to stretch as we awaited further instructions from the flight deck. With each passing minute, I remained vigilant, ready to adapt to any changes in the patient's condition. The entire ordeal had brought a sudden and unexpected urgency to my vacation, but my commitment to the well-being of the passenger remained unwavering.

Finally, after what felt like an eternity, the pilot's voice came over the intercom. We had been in contact with medical professionals on the ground who had provided guidance on managing the situation. It was determined that we could continue the flight to our destination, and the passenger's condition had stabilized sufficiently for us to do so.

As we resumed our journey toward Hawaii, the atmosphere on the plane shifted from one of anxiety to one of relief and gratitude. The other passengers, who had witnessed the medical emergency, expressed their appreciation for the assistance provided. It was a humbling moment, a reminder of the interconnectedness of humanity even in the midst of a vacation-bound flight.

For the remainder of the journey, I continued to monitor the unconscious passenger, her condition gradually improving. The flight attendants and I remained vigilant, ready to respond to any changes. It was a surreal experience, the unexpected twist in my vacation plans serving as a stark reminder of the unpredictable nature of life.

Upon landing in Hawaii, the passenger was transferred to a local hospital for further evaluation and care. I offered my contact information to the flight attendants; in case they needed any additional information or assistance related to the incident. It was a curious moment as I bid farewell to the plane and its passengers. I boarded the plane and was going one way to Hawaii but my vacation decided to take another route.

CHAPTER TWELVE

SHE ATE HER WEIGHT

IN MY YEARS as a medical professional, I've encountered a diverse array of patients with a wide range of medical conditions. Yet, nothing could have prepared me for the day I met Meekah, a remarkable woman who presented an equally remarkable medical anomaly that left both me and my colleagues utterly perplexed. The experience of working with her was nothing short of extraordinary, and I'd like to share this incredible journey of discovery with you. Meekah was a 32-year-old woman who walked into our clinic one sunny morning in the early spring. Her presence was unassuming, her smile welcoming, but her medical history was far from ordinary. She had been referred to us by another medical center after a battery of tests had failed to provide any definitive answers regarding her condition. Little did I know that this encounter would lead me down a path of fascination and intrigue.

Meekah's chief complaint was something that defied explanation: she had an insatiable appetite, yet she had never gained a single pound in her entire life. Her journey into the enigmatic world of medicine began during her childhood when her parents first noticed that, despite her insatiable appetite and seemingly endless consumption of food, she remained as slender as ever. In a world where many struggled with obesity, Meekah's situation was the polar opposite. Meekah's case was an enigma wrapped in a medical mystery, and my team and I were determined to get to the bottom of it. We embarked on a comprehensive medical evaluation, commencing with a thorough physical examination. To our amazement, Meekah was the epitome of health; there were no signs of underlying medical conditions that might explain her inability to gain weight. Her vital signs were all stable, her blood pressure and heart rate well within the normal range, and her overall health was excellent. Next, we delved into her extensive medical history, hoping to uncover any clues that might shed light on her condition. Meekah had undergone a plethora of tests and consultations with various specialists throughout her life, including endocrinologists, gastroenterologists, and nutritionists. Yet, despite their best efforts, no one had been able to provide her with a concrete diagnosis or a viable solution to her unique predicament. Meekah's appetite was not merely robust; it was voracious. She could consume enormous quantities of food without ever feeling full. Her diet was rich in calories and consisted of everything from high-calorie desserts to hearty, nutrient-dense meals. She never restricted herself, and yet her weight remained constant. The paradox was nothing short of baffling.

Our initial step was to conduct a very wide variety of tests, including a comprehensive blood panel, thyroid function tests, and metabolic assessments. Much to our frustration, every result came back well within normal ranges, ruling out common metabolic disorders and hormonal imbalances. Meekah's body appeared to function perfectly, with no apparent impediments to weight gain. One of the most puzzling aspects of Meekah's case was that her condition seemed entirely isolated. No one else in her family had experienced anything remotely similar. Her parents, siblings, and extended family members were all of average weight and had never faced any metabolic or dietary issues. As we continued our investigation, we explored less common medical conditions, such as malabsorption syndromes and gastroin-testinal disorders that might interfere with nutrient absorption. However, Meekah's gastrointestinal tract appeared to function normally, absorbing nutrients as efficiently as anyone else's. What intrigued us even more was that Meekah's body seemed to metabolize calories at a rate that defied conventional understanding. We meticulously calculated her daily caloric intake and expenditure, and the numbers simply didn't align. She was consuming far more calories than should have been required to maintain her weight, yet her body remained seemingly impervious to the effects of her food consumption.

As we delved deeper into the science of metabolism, we stumbled upon an intriguing possibility – a rare genetic condition known as "congenital leptin deficien-cy." Leptin, a hormone produced by fat cells, plays a pivotal role in regulating appetite and metabolism. In individuals with congenital leptin deficiency, the absence of this hormone results in insatiable hunger and an inability to sense fullness. Our curiosity piqued, we decided to pursue genetic testing to explore this poten-tial avenue. The results that followed were nothing short of astonishing. Meekah, indeed, had a genetic mutation that resulted in a complete lack of leptin production. This discovery was groundbreaking, as it provided a plausible explanation for her insatiable appetite and inability to gain weight. With the diagnosis in hand, our journey to understand and treat Meekah's unique condition was just beginning. Congenital leptin deficiency was rare, and managing it required a highly tailored approach. We knew that providing Meekah with the best possible care would involve ongoing monitoring, precise adjustments to her treatment plan, and a multidisciplinary team of experts. Meekah's leptin replacement therapy started cautiously. We began with carefully measured doses, keeping a close eye on her appetite, metabolic responses, and any potential side effects. In the initial weeks, we conducted frequent check-ins, allowing Meekah to voice any concerns and ensuring she felt comfortable with the treatment regimen. One of the immediate changes Meekah noticed was a reduction in her relentless hunger. For the first time in her life, she began to experience a sense of fullness after meals. It was a revelation, a feeling that had eluded her for as long as she could remember. As her treatment progressed, she found herself not only eating less but also making healthier food choices, no longer compelled to consume vast quantities of high-calorie foods.

The transformation was not only physical but also psychological. Meekah's relationship with food had been a source of constant struggle and frustration. With leptin replacement therapy, she gained a newfound sense of control over her eating habits. The psychological burden of her condition began to lift, and she felt empowered to make healthier choices that would benefit her long-term health. As the months passed, Meekah's body underwent remarkable changes. Her weight, which had remained stagnant for years, began to inch upward. It was a slow and steady process, but it marked a significant milestone in her journey. Her energy levels improved, and she no longer experienced the constant fatigue that had plagued her before. One of the most critical aspects of managing congenital leptin deficiency was the need for vigilant monitoring. We conducted regular blood tests to measure Meekah's leptin levels and assess her overall metabolic health. Adjustments to her leptin replacement therapy were made as needed to ensure that she received the optimal dose for her unique physiology.

What made Meekah's case even more fascinating was her enthusiastic participation in her own medical journey. She diligently kept a food diary, documenting her meals, portion sizes, and any changes in appetite. Her detailed records provided invaluable insights into how leptin replacement therapy was affecting her and guided our decision-making process. Meekah's story was not just about medical intervention; it was a testament to the profound impact that patient engagement and collaboration could have on the success of treatment. Her willingness to actively participate in her care set a powerful example for both our medical team and other patients facing rare medical conditions.

As Meekah continued to progress, we knew that her case would serve as a vital reference point for future research into congenital leptin deficiency. While her condition was rare, it raised essential questions about the role of leptin in regulating appetite and metabolism in the broader context of human health. The insights we gained from Meekah's journey had the potential to inform the development of more effective treatments for metabolic disorders. Meekah's case also highlighted the importance of genetic counseling and family education. While Meekah was the first in her family to be diagnosed with congenital leptin deficiency, her genetic mutation could potentially be passed on to her children. Genetic counseling allowed her to make informed decisions about family planning, ensuring that future generations would have access to the same level of care and understanding. As Meekah's story continued to unfold, we couldn't help but be inspired by her resilience and determination. Her journey had not been easy, but she had faced every challenge with grace and a positive attitude. Her experience underscored the importance of support systems for patients with rare medical conditions, and we were grateful to have been a part of her journey. One of the most profound moments in Meekah's journey came when she attended a support group for individuals with rare genetic conditions. It was the first time she had met others who shared her experiences, and the sense of camaraderie was palpable. In that room, she found a community of people who understood the challenges and triumphs of living with a rare medical anomaly.

Meekah's participation in the support group also brought attention to the importance of patient advocacy. She became a vocal advocate for individuals with congenital leptin deficiency, raising awareness about the condition and advocating for increased research funding. Her efforts played a pivotal role in bringing attention to the unique challenges faced by those with rare genetic conditions. The impact of her journey extended beyond the realm of medical science. It was a testament to the power of human resilience and the capacity to overcome even the most daunting challenges. Her story served as an inspiration to others facing rare medical conditions, reminding them that they were not alone in their struggles.

As Meekah's case became more widely known, it

also raised questions about the broader implications of genetic testing and precision medicine. The ability to diagnose and treat rare genetic conditions was a promising frontier in modern medicine, offering hope to individuals who had long felt isolated by their conditions. Meekah's experience highlighted the need for continued investment in genetic research and personalized medicine. Her journey had demonstrated that even the most perplexing medical mysteries could be unraveled with the right combination of scientific inquiry and patient-centered care. It was a testament to the potential for medical science to transform lives and offer new possibilities for those facing rare and enigmatic conditions.

In the years that followed, Meekah's story continued to inspire both our medical team and the broader medical community. Her ongoing participation in clinical research and her dedication to advocacy became a driving force for progress in the field of rare genetic conditions. Her legacy was not just one of resilience but also one of hope and the potential for a brighter future for individuals facing similar challenges. Personally, I believe Meekah's case underscores the importance of collaboration between patients, medical professionals, and researchers in advancing our understanding of rare genetic conditions and improving the lives of individuals like Meekah.

Meekah's journey also highlighted the importance of interdisciplinary collaboration in solving medical mysteries. It took the combined expertise of physicians, geneticists, and nutritionists to unravel the complexities of her condition. The experience emphasized the significance of teamwork and shared knowledge in the ever-evolving field of medicine. More than any other case I've ever worked on throughout my decades long career, Meekah's highlighted the fact for me, that with each medical anomaly we encounter, we are pushed to expand our boundaries, challenge our assumptions, and ultimately, to become better healers and scientists.

I think about Meekah often and wonder how she is doing and what became of her life after we were finally able to help her. I like to think of her living happily somewhere out in the world and I smile when I think of her bright smile which, even when she was at her lowest points and even when we were seemingly unable to come up with a solution for her, lit up every room she walked into. Meekah's legacy serves as a beacon of hope for the future of rare genetic condition research. With each step forward, we draw closer to unlocking the mysteries of these enigmatic conditions and providing the answers and solutions that individuals like Meekah so rightfully deserve.

CONTINUE WITH
CRASH: STORIES FROM THE EMERGENCY
ROOM: VOLUME 4

ABOUT THE AUTHOR

Dr. David Berg is a highly skilled and compassionate doctor, specializing in internal medicine. With a passion for patient care, he excels in connecting with individuals on a deep level. Driven by a thirst for knowledge, he has contributed to groundbreaking research and established clinics in underserved communities. His gentle demeanor and commitment to personalized care have made him a beloved figure in the medical community. Dr. David Berg is a beacon of hope, transforming lives and inspiring others to create a healthier world.

He loves humor, his work, as well as his wife and family. He lives north of Houston, in the great state of Texas.

ALSO BY DAVID BERG, M.D.

STAT: CRAZY MEDICAL STORIES

CRASH: STORIES FROM THE EMERGENCY ROOM

ALSO BY FREE REIGN PUBLISHING

Made in the USA
Las Vegas, NV
17 April 2024

88800204R00100